Medical Coding in the Real World Student Workbook

Elizabeth Roberts

MA Ed, CPC

AHIMA
PRESS

ISBN: 978-1-58426-559-7
AHIMA Product No.: AC235016

AHIMA Staff:
Chelsea Brotherton, MA, Assistant Editor
Megan Grennan, Managing Editor

Cover image: ©ivanastar, iStockphoto

For more information, including updates, about AHIMA Press publications, visit http://www.ahima.org/education/press.

American Health Information Management Association
233 North Michigan Avenue, 21st Floor
Chicago, Illinois 60601-5809
ahima.org

Brief Table of Contents

About the Author

Elizabeth Roberts, MA Ed, CPC, is the Allied Health Program Director for the Computer Career Center, a division of Vista College in Las Cruces, NM, and is an AHIMA-Approved ICD-10 CM/PCS Trainer. Mrs. Roberts has a master's degree in Education and extensive experience in healthcare reimbursement and medical coding. In addition to serving as the lead instructor for the Medical Billing and Coding Department for Virginia College in Austin, Texas, she also spent three years as the senior director of content for ImplementHIT, a healthcare information technology company specializing in bite-sized educational modules for medical providers and clinical staff. An experienced consultant in medical coding and reimbursement, including practice management, HIPAA, compliance, insurance regulations, and medical coding (CPT, ICD-10, HCPCS), she enjoys helping billers, coders, clinical staff, and providers unweave the complicated tangle of coding and billing, in order to optimize healthcare reimbursement.

How to Use This Workbook

Medical Coding in the Real World, Student Workbook is a comprehensive student workbook designed to enhance important information addressed in each chapter of *Medical Coding in the Real World*, and to reinforce learning through practice. This student workbook includes 20 chapters, each of which corresponds to the information presented in the textbook. Each workbook chapter includes several true/false, multiple choice, matching, short answer, and coding exercises.

The student workbook is meant to be a companion to the textbook, and should be used in conjunction with the textbook, chapter by chapter. In this manner, the workbook should be used to reinforce the information learned in each chapter of the text, and to provide practice selecting, sequencing, and reporting the appropriate ICD-10-CM, CPT, HCPCS, and ICD-10-PCS codes, as necessary.

Acknowledgments

The author and AHIMA Press would like to acknowledge Gloria Anderson, MEd, RHIA, CCS; Tina L. Cressman, CCS, CCS-P, CPC CPC-H CPC-P CEMC; Lauree E. Handlon, MS, RHIA, CCS, COC, FAHIMA; and Linda A. Hyde, RHIA for their valuable contributions to the textbook and workbook.

Part I

Medical Billing and Coding Basics

CHAPTER 1

Your Coding Career

Vocabulary

Instructions: Define each of the following key terms in the space provided.

1. Administrative personnel: _____

_____

_____

2. Ambulatory surgical center (ASC): _____

_____

_____

3. American Health Information Management Association (AHIMA): _____

_____

_____

4. Certified Coding Specialist (CCS): _____

_____

_____

5. Classification system: _____

_____

_____

6. Clinical personnel: _____

_____

_____

7. Coding certification: _____

_____

_____

8. Continuing education unit (CEU): _____

_____

_____

9. Date of service: _____

_____

_____

10. Diagnosis: _____

_____

_____

11. Emergency department: _____

_____

_____

12. Encounter: _____

_____

_____

13. Healthcare billing: _____

_____

_____

14. Healthcare coding: _____

_____

_____

15. Healthcare provider: _____

_____

_____

16. Healthcare specialty: _____

_____

_____

17. Hospital: _____

_____

_____

18. Inpatient: _____

_____

_____

19. Internal medicine provider: _____

_____

_____

20. Large group practice: _____

_____

_____

21. Mid-level provider: _____

_____

_____

22. Outpatient: _____

_____

_____

23. Physician: _____

_____

_____

24. Primary care provider (PCP): _____

_____

_____

25. Procedure: _____

_____

_____

26. Professional organization: _____

_____

_____

27. Remote coding: _____

_____

_____

28. Small group practice: _____

_____

_____

29. Solo practice: _____

_____

_____

30. Surgical specialist: _____

_____

_____

31. Urgent care facility: _____

_____

_____

Matching

Instructions: Match the terms with the appropriate descriptions.

1. _____ Primary Care Provider (PCP)

2. _____ Specialty Provider

3. _____ Pediatrician

4. _____ Family Practice

5. _____ General Practitioner

6. _____ Internal Medicine

7. _____ Obstetrics and Gynecology

8. _____ Holistic and Integrative Specialists

9. _____ Behavioral Health

10. _____ Allergy/Immunology

11. _____ Anesthesiology and Pain Management

12. _____ Cardiology

A. Specializes in conditions affecting the feet

B. Treats adult patients and specializes in the health of the entire body, including health maintenance and preventive care

C. Specializes in a particular area of medical expertise, including diagnosis, management, and treatment

D. Treats patients from birth to elderly

E. Specializes in the prevention and treatment of adult internal diseases

F. Specializes in disorders of the immune system

G. Treats patients ages 0 to 18

H. Provides whole-health care, maintains patient health history, and performs preventive examinations and services

I. Specializes in the diagnosis and treatment of the cardiovascular system; can be surgical, invasive, non-invasive, or specializes in treatment strategies

J. Specializes in conditions affecting the kidneys

K. Specializes in women's health, pregnancy, and childbirth; includes labor and delivery, maternal fetal medicine, fertility services, and midwife services

L. Specializes in whole-body health with an emphasis on holistic techniques, such as acupuncture

Matching continued on next page

(Continued)

13. _____ Surgical Specialist

M. Specializes in anesthesia services and the treatment and management of pain

14. _____ Therapy and Rehabilitation

N. Specializes in the testing or pathology and laboratory specimens

15. _____ Laboratory and Pathology

O. Specializes in performing and developing therapeutic and rehabilitative services for patients

16. _____ Neurology

P. Specializes in performing and developing surgical techniques for each respective body system or organ

17. _____ Orthopedics

Q. Specializes in geriatric medicine for elderly patients

18. _____ Dermatology

R. Specializes in the mental health of patients, includes psychiatric services and addiction medicine

19. _____ Geriatric Medicine

S. Specializes in diagnosis and treatment of orthopedic conditions, such as fractures and osteoporosis

20. _____ Hematology and Oncology

T. Specializes in ailments of the endocrine system, such as diabetes mellitus

21. _____ Gastroenterology

U. Specializes in the detection, management, and treatment of blood conditions and malignancies

22. _____ Radiology and Imaging

V. Specializes in diagnosis and treatment of conditions affecting the neurological system

23. _____ Endocrinology

W. Specializes in conditions affecting the gastrointestinal system

24. _____ Hospice and Palliative Care

X. Specializes in the detection, treatment, and management of infectious diseases, such as HIV

25. _____ Infectious Disease

Y. Provides end-of life treatment for terminally ill patients

26. _____ Nephrology

Z. Specializes in the performance of either diagnostic or therapeutic radiology services, in addition to other types of imaging services

27. _____ Ophthalmology/ Optometry

AA. Specializes in the dermatological system (skin)

28. _____ Otolaryngology

BB. Specializes in the detection and treatment of eye conditions and vision services

29. _____ Podiatry

CC. Specializes in the urological system and the male reproductive system

30. _____ Rheumatology

DD. Specializes in rheumatism, arthritis, and other disorders of the joints

31. _____ Urology

EE. Specializes in the ears, nose, and throat

True/False

Instructions: Indicate whether the following statements are true or false (T or F). For false statements, rewrite the statement on the line below to make the statement true.

1. To be successful as an online coder, you must have a lot of self-discipline.

   _____

   _____

2. A large group practice is more likely to be multi-specialty.

   _____

   _____

3. A solo group practice has only one doctor.

   _____

   _____

4. If you work in a large clinic, you are more likely to have to perform multiple responsibilities throughout the clinic.

   _____

   _____

5. If you work in a small clinic, you are likely to have a more detailed job description with fewer job responsibilities.

_____

_____

6. In the inpatient facility setting, ICD-10-PCS codes are used to identify diagnoses.

_____

_____

7. In the outpatient professional setting, ICD-10-CM codes are used to identify diagnoses.

_____

_____

8. HCPCS codes are used to identify supplies and services in the inpatient facility setting.

_____

_____

9. CPT codes are used to identify procedures in the outpatient setting.

_____

_____

10. A mid-level provider has a medical doctorate degree, such as an MD or a DO.

_____

_____

Multiple Choice

Instructions: Choose the best answer.

1. In which of the following settings can you work as a medical coder?
   a. Billing and coding company
   b. Outpatient practices and inpatient facilities
   c. Outpatient practices only
   d. All three: billing and coding companies, outpatient practices, and inpatient facilities

2. Which of the following medical practices can either be standalone or attached to a hospital, and provide services on an emergent setting?
   a. Large group practice
   b. Hospital
   c. Ambulatory surgical center (ASC)
   d. Emergency department

3. Which of the following types of medical practices would be composed of four physicians, all of whom practice the same specialty?
   a. Solo practice
   b. Small group practice
   c. Large groups practice
   d. Hospital

4. National Healthcare is a group practice made up of seven physicians. Three of the doctors practice internal medicine and the other four doctors practice women's health. How would this practice be classified?
   a. Small group
   b. Multi-specialty
   c. Single-specialty
   d. Ambulatory surgical center (ASC)

5. Which of the following would also be referred to as an acute-care facility?
   a. Outpatient clinic
   b. Hospice and palliative care facility
   c. Inpatient facility
   d. Rehabilitation facility

6. Why is it important to understand the differences between inpatient facility reporting and outpatient professional reporting?
   a. Because the codes reported differ
   b. Because coders do not work in inpatient facilities
   c. Because some facilities are larger than others
   d. Inpatient facility and outpatient professional reporting are the same

7. Which of the following is a type of medical practice in which a provider specializes after completing medical school?
   a. A healthcare specialty
   b. Primary care
   c. A mid-level provider
   d. A solo practitioner

8. What type of medical provider specializes in diagnosing and treating the entire patient, including health maintenance and preventive health screenings?
   a. A primary care provider (PCP)
   b. A medical specialist
   c. A solo practitioner
   d. An internal medicine doctor

9. Who sends the referral or prior authorization request for patients?
a. The medical specialist
b. The primary care provider
c. The internal medicine doctor
d. The hospital or inpatient facility

10. Which of the following can be an inpatient facility?
a. Ambulatory surgical center (ASC)
b. Hospital
c. Physician office
d. Urgent care clinic

CHAPTER 2

Healthcare Billing Basics

Vocabulary

Instructions: Define each of the following key terms in the space provided.

1. Accountable care organization (ACO): _____

_____

_____

2. Accreditation: _____

_____

_____

3. Administrative safeguards: _____

_____

_____

4. Advanced beneficiary notice (ABN): _____

_____

_____

5. Business associates (BAs): _____

_____

_____

6. Capitation: _____

_____

_____

7. Centers for Medicare and Medicaid Services (CMS): _____

_____

_____

8. Charge amount: _____

_____

_____

9. Children's Health Insurance Program (CHIP): _____

_____

_____

10. CMS-1500: _____

_____

_____

11. Coinsurance: _____

_____

_____

12. Commercial insurance: _____

_____

_____

13. Comorbidity: _____

_____

_____

14. Complication: _____

_____

_____

15. Computerized physician order entry (CPOE): _____

_____

_____

16. Confidentiality agreement: _____

_____

_____

17. Copayment: _____

_____

_____

18. Coverage limitations: _____

_____

_____

19. Covered entities: _____

_____

_____

20. Data analytics: _____

_____

_____

21. Deductible: _____

_____

_____

22. De-identified documentation: _____

_____

_____

23. Electronic Protected Health Information (e-PHI): _____

_____

_____

24. Employer-sponsored insurance: _____

_____

_____

25. Encryption: _____

_____

_____

26. Enforcement Rule: _____

_____

_____

27. Entitlement health insurance: _____

_____

_____

28. Fee schedule: _____

_____

_____

29. Fee-for-service: _____

_____

_____

30. Government-sponsored insurance: _____

_____

_____

31. HCC coding: _____

_____

_____

32. Health insurance exchange: _____

_____

_____

33. Health Insurance Marketplace: _____

_____

_____

34. Health Insurance Portability and Accountability Act (HIPAA): _____

_____

_____

35. Healthcare operations: _____

_____

_____

36. Hierarchical Condition Categories (HCC): _____

_____

_____

37. Individual insurance: _____

_____

_____

38. Insurance policy: _____

_____

_____

39. Insured party: _____

_____

_____

40. Medicaid: _____

_____

_____

41. Medical necessity: _____

_____

_____

42. Medicare: _____

_____

_____

43. Medigap: _____

_____

_____

44. Minimum necessary: _____

_____

_____

45. Noncovered services: _____

_____

_____

46. Notice of Privacy Practices: _____

_____

_____

47. Out-of-pocket expense: _____

_____

_____

48. Patient Centered Medical Home (PCMH): _____

_____

_____

49. Payment: _____

_____

_____

50. Performance measures: _____

_____

_____

51. Per member per month (PMPM): _____

_____

_____

52. Physical safeguards: _____

_____

_____

53. Premium: _____

_____

_____

54. Prior authorization (PA): _____

_____

_____

55. Privacy Rule: _____

_____

_____

56. Prospective payment system (PPS): _____

_____

_____

57. Protected health information (PHI): _____

_____

_____

58. Provider contracting: _____

_____

_____

59. Quality improvement (QI): _____

_____

_____

60. Referral: _____

_____

_____

61. Reimbursement: _____

_____

_____

62. Risk adjustment: _____

_____

_____

63. Risk analysis: _____

_____

_____

64. Security Rule: _____

_____

_____

65. Supplemental insurance: _____

_____

_____

66. Technical safeguards: _____

_____

_____

67. Third-party payer: _____

_____

_____

68. Treatment: _____

_____

_____

69. Treatment, payment, and healthcare operations (TPO): _____

_____

_____

70. TRICARE: _____

_____

_____

71. UB-04: _____

_____

_____

72. Worker's compensation insurance: _____

_____

_____

True/False

Instructions: Indicate whether the following statements are true or false (T or F). For false statements, rewrite the statement on the line below to make the statement true.

1. HIPAA covered entities include health plans, clearinghouses, and healthcare providers.

   _____

   _____

2. PHI stands for patient health information.

   _____

   _____

3. PHI may be released for treatment, payment, and healthcare operations.

   _____

   _____

4. Administrative, technical, and physical safeguards are all components of the Privacy Rule.

   _____

   _____

5. The UB-04 claim form is used for outpatient professional billing.

_____

_____

6. A coinsurance is a preset amount that must be paid in full before insurance benefits will begin.

_____

_____

7. The total charge amount for a professional outpatient claim is entered in box 28.

_____

_____

8. An ABN should be issued to a patient when it is expected that Medicare will not pay for a service.

_____

_____

9. Capitation is a form of reimbursement that is based on an amount charged for each service performed.

_____

_____

10. HCC stands for Hierarchical Coding Conditions.

_____

_____

Multiple Choice

Instructions: Choose the best answer.

1. Which of the following HIPAA rules sets standards for the protection of personal health information by covered entities?
   a. Privacy Rule
   b. Security Rule
   c. Enforcement Rule
   d. Health Insurance Portability and Accountability Act

2. Which of the following is considered PHI?
   a. Information related to the patient's educational background and history
   b. Information related to the patient's credit history
   c. Information related to the provision of healthcare to the patient
   d. Information regarding the patient's homeowner's insurance

3. Which of the following principles states that only information that is directly related to TPO should be released?
   a. Medical necessity
   b. Treatment, payment, and healthcare operations (TPO)
   c. Minimum necessary
   d. Protected health information (PHI)

4. Which of the following evaluates the likelihood that a security breach would happen in a healthcare organization?
   a. Risk adjustment
   b. CPOE
   c. Encryption
   d. Risk analysis

5. Which of the following documents is signed by the patient to indicate that they have been made aware of the practice's policies related to patient privacy?
   a. Confidentiality agreement
   b. Notice of privacy practices
   c. Business associate agreement
   d. Covered entity agreement

6. Reimbursement is another word for which of the following?
   a. The amount charged for a service
   b. The write-off amount
   c. The billed amount
   d. The amount paid

7. Which medical claim form should be used to bill outpatient professional claims?
   a. CMS-1450
   b. UB-04
   c. CMS-1500
   d. Both the UB-04 and CMS-1500 may be used

8. In which section of the CMS-1500 form are diagnosis and procedure codes entered?
   a. Carrier information
   b. Physician or supplier information
   c. Patient and insured information
   d. Both physician or supplier information and patient and insured information

9. How many CPT or HCPCS codes may be entered on a single CMS-1500 claim form?
   a. 6
   b. 8
   c. 12
   d. 4

10. Which of the following is an amount of money that a patient must pay before they may be seen by the medical provider?
   a. Deductible
   b. Coinsurance
   c. Copayment
   d. Noncovered service fee

11. Which of the following types of insurance is purchased by a person who does attain coverage via his or her employer?
   a. Employer-sponsored insurance
   b. Individual insurance
   c. Government-sponsored insurance
   d. Entitlement health insurance

12. Which of the following is a government-sponsored insurance that provides coverage for patients who are elderly or disabled?
   a. Medicare
   b. Medicaid
   c. Worker's compensation
   d. TRICARE

13. Which of the following is an example of a supplemental insurance plan?
   a. TRICARE
   b. Worker's compensation
   c. Medigap
   d. Homeowner's insurance

14. If the patient's insurance does not authorize the services of a medical specialist via a prior authorization or referral, who is responsible for paying for the service, if provided?
   a. The patient
   b. The specialist
   c. The patient's insurance
   d. The referring provider

15. Which of the following is a group of medical providers that coordinate to provide high-quality care for their patients?
   a. CMS
   b. ACO
   c. HIPAA
   d. HCC

3
CHAPTER

Basics of Coding

Vocabulary

Instructions: Define each of the following key terms in the space provided.

1. Clinical modification (CM): _____

_____

_____

2. Code linkage: _____

_____

_____

3. Coding guidelines: _____

_____

_____

4. Current Procedural Terminology (CPT): _____

_____

_____

5. Evaluation and management (E/M) service: _____

_____

_____

6. HCPCS Level I codes: _____

_____

_____

7. HCPCS Level II codes: _____

_____

_____

8. Healthcare Common Procedure Coding System (HCPCS): _____

_____

_____

9. Healthcare codes: _____

_____

_____

10. ICD-10-CM: _____

_____

_____

11. ICD-10-PCS: _____

_____

_____

12. ICD-11: _____

_____

_____

13. ICD-9: _____

_____

_____

14. International Classification of Diseases (ICD): _____

_____

_____

15. Legacy system: _____

_____

_____

16. Medical necessity: _____

_____

_____

17. Modifier: _____

_____

_____

18. Procedural coding system (PCS): _____

_____

_____

True/False

Instructions: Indicate whether the following statements are true or false (T or F). For false statements, rewrite the statement on the line below to make the statement true.

1. The CMS-1500 form is the numeric or alphanumeric translation of all of the services, supplies, treatments, diagnoses, conditions, and other reasons for medical treatments.

_____

_____

2. ICD codes are now in their tenth revision, which went into effect on October 1, 1993.

_____

_____

3. HCPCS Level II codes are also known simply as HCPCS codes.

_____

_____

4. In fee-for-service payment, CPT codes are directly attached to a charge for the procedure performed on a patient.

_____

_____

5. HCPCS manuals are published on October 1st of each year.

_____

_____

6. The information compiled from the analysis of healthcare codes is also used for risk adjustment and performance measurement.

_____

_____

7. Code linkage is identifying the HCC score for each procedure performed on a patient.

_____

_____

8. If it is not documented, it never happened.

_____

_____

9. Coding guidelines are the rules that specify which codes to use in given situations, how to sequence them, and how much the insurance will reimburse for them.

_____

_____

10. A CPT modifier identifies additional information regarding the service provided.

_____

_____

Multiple Choice

Instructions: Choose the best answer.

1. On which date are ICD-10-CM codes updated each year?
a. October 1st
b. January 1st
c. Quarterly
d. Both January 1st and October 1st

2. On which date are CPT codes updated each year?
a. October 1st
b. January 1st
c. Quarterly
d. Both January 1st and October 1st

3. How often are HCPCS codes updated?
   a. Annually
   b. Bi-annually
   c. Quarterly
   d. Once every two years

4. Which healthcare code is used to identify procedures performed in the outpatient setting?
   a. ICD-10-CM
   b. ICD-10-PCS
   c. CPT
   d. CDT

5. Which healthcare code set is used to identify the patient's diagnosis or other reason for the encounter?
   a. ICD-10-CM
   b. ICD-10-PCS
   c. CPT
   d. CDT

6. Which of the following code sets will replace ICD-10 in the future?
   a. ICD-9
   b. ICD-10-PCS
   c. ICD-11-PCS
   d. ICD-11

7. The ICD-9 code set is important to understand because of which of the following?
   a. It is used on current claims to identify medical necessity for services provided.
   b. It is a legacy coding system that may be used by non-HIPAA covered entities.
   c. It was used on claims before October 1st, 2015 to identify procedures provided to patients.
   d. The ICD-9 code set has not been in use since 1975 and it not important to understand.

8. Level II HCPCS codes are also referred to as:
   a. ICD-10-CM
   b. ICD-10-PCS
   c. CPT
   d. HCPCS

9. Medical necessity for the service performed is identified by which of the following healthcare codes?
   a. ICD-10-CM
   b. ICD-10-PCS
   c. CPT
   d. HCPCS

10. Which of the following is a two-digit code used to add additional information to a procedural description?

a. PCS

b. CM

c. HCC

d. Modifier

Short Answer

Instructions: Using the two questions What did the doctor do? *and* Why did the doctor do it?*, identify the procedures and diagnoses from the following statements. (Only identify the diagnosis and procedure, do not look up the codes for either.)*

1. Derrick presented to the office of his gastroenterologist for a screening colonoscopy. GI doctor performed the colonoscopy, during which two colonic polyps were identified and removed with a cold knife. They were later determined to be benign.

Procedure: _____

Diagnosis: _____

2. Jaime presented to the emergency department with a laceration on his right arm due to a landscaping accident. ER doctor performed a simple wound repair of the 5 cm laceration.

Procedure: _____

Diagnosis: _____

3. Patient at 38 weeks' gestation of pregnancy presented to labor and delivery in active labor. Obstetrician vaginally delivered a newborn male infant after 4 hours of uncomplicated labor.

Procedure: _____

Diagnosis: _____

Instructions: Answer the following question or prompt in one to three sentences.

4. Explain code linkage and how it is related to medical necessity and payment for healthcare services.

_____

_____

_____

5. Explain how billing and coding are connected and why it is important for coders to understand the basics of healthcare billing.

_____

_____

_____

Code Linkage

Code linkage is identified on the CMS-1500 claim form by adding the letter that corresponds to each diagnosis in box 24.E for each procedure billed on the claim. For example, see the following figure that demonstrates how to link codes together. In the following figure, the diagnosis codes for swimmer's ear, H60.332— listed on line A—is linked with the first procedure code on the claim, 99213, for the office evaluation. In this case the swimmer's ear diagnosis code is linked to the office evaluation procedure code by adding the letter A to box 24.E. Similarly, the diagnosis code for the wart, B07.9—listed on line B—is linked to the procedure code for cryosurgery, 17000, the second procedure on the claim, by adding the letter B in box 24.E.

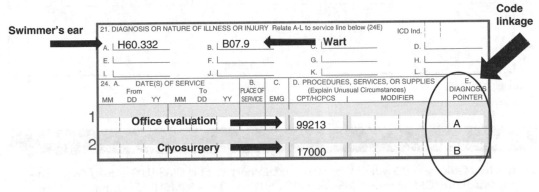

Source: CMS 2017.

In the following exercise, link the diagnosis codes to the procedure codes on the claim by adding the appropriate letter in box 24.E.

1. Clinic Note:

A 40-year-old established female presented to the office for a routine preventive exam. After performing a comprehensive physical examination with no abnormal findings, the provider also administered the annual flu vaccine to the patient.

Diagnosis Codes Reported:

- Z00.00, Encounter for general adult medical examination without abnormal findings
- Z23, Encounter for immunization

Procedure Codes Reported:

- 99396, Periodic comprehensive preventive medicine reevalution and management of an individual…; 40-64 years
- 90471, Immunization administration…; 1 vaccine
- 90658, Influenza virus vaccine, trivalent (IIV3), split virus, 0.5 mL dosage, for intramuscular use

Link the diagnosis codes to the appropriate procedure codes in the area below by adding the correct diagnosis pointer(s) in box 24.E for procedure codes one through three.

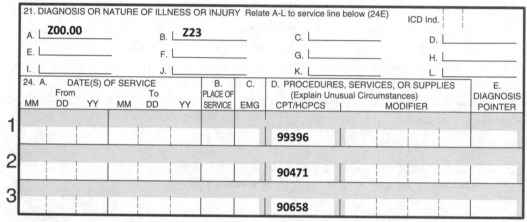

Source: CMS 2017.

Reference

Centers for Medicare and Medicaid Services. 2017. Details for title: CMS 1500. https://www.cms
.gov/Medicare/CMS-Forms/CMS-Forms/CMS-Forms-Items/CMS1188854.html.

CHAPTER 4

Learning the ICD-10-CM Code Book

Vocabulary

Instructions: Define each of the following key terms in the space provided.

1. Accidental intent: _____

_____

_____

2. Activity: _____

_____

_____

3. Acute conditions: _____

_____

_____

4. Adverse effect: _____

_____

_____

5. Assault: _____

_____

_____

HCC

6. Benign neoplasm: _____

_____

_____

7. Bilateral: _____

_____

_____

8. Billable code: _____

_____

_____

9. Carcinoma in situ: _____

_____

_____

10. Chronic condition: _____

_____

_____

11. Code first: _____

_____

_____

12. Combination code: _____

_____

_____

13. Cross-reference: _____

_____

_____

14. Definitive diagnosis: _____

_____

_____

15. Episode of care: _____

_____

_____

16. Essential modifier: _____

_____

_____

17. Etiology: _____

_____

_____

18. Excludes notes: _____

_____

_____

19. Excludes1: _____

_____

_____

20. Excludes2: _____

_____

_____

21. External cause codes: _____

_____

_____

22. External Causes of Injury Index: _____

_____

_____

23. First-listed diagnosis: _____

_____

_____

24. Histologic type: _____

_____

_____

25. Includes notes: _____

_____

_____

26. Inclusion terms: _____

_____

_____

27. Index to Diseases and Injury: _____

_____

_____

28. Initial encounter: _____

_____

_____

29. Injury mechanism: _____

_____

_____

30. Intent: _____

_____

_____

31. Intentional self-harm: _____

_____

_____

32. Invalid code: _____

_____

_____

33. Laterality: _____

_____

_____

34. Main term: _____

_____

_____

35. Malignant neoplasm: _____

_____

_____

36. Manifestation: _____

_____

_____

37. Metastasis: _____

_____

_____

38. Morphology: _____

_____

_____

39. Neoplasm: _____

_____

_____

40. Neoplasm of uncertain behavior: _____

_____

_____

41. Nonessential modifier: _____

_____

_____

42. Not elsewhere classifiable (NEC): _____

_____

_____

43. Not otherwise specified (NOS): _____

_____

_____

44. Official Guidelines for Coding and Reporting (OGCR): _____

_____

_____

45. Patient status: _____

_____

_____

46. Place of occurrence: _____

_____

_____

47. Placeholder X: _____

_____

_____

48. Primary neoplasm: _____

_____

_____

49. Secondary neoplasm: _____

_____

_____

50. See also: _____

_____

_____

51. See condition: _____

_____

_____

52. Sequela: _____

_____

_____

53. Sequencing: _____

_____

_____

54. Seventh character extension: _____

_____

_____

55. Signs: _____

_____

_____

56. Specificity: _____

_____

_____

57. Subsequent encounter: _____

_____

_____

58. Subterm: _____

_____

_____

59. Symptoms: _____

_____

_____

60. Table of Drugs and Chemicals: _____

_____

_____

61. Table of Neoplasms: _____

_____

_____

62. Tabular List: _____

_____

_____

63. Toxic effect: _____

_____

_____

64. Underdosing: _____

_____

_____

65. Undetermined intent: _____

_____

_____

66. Use additional code: _____

_____

_____

Fill in the Blank

Instructions: Complete the following statements.

1. The _____ is the cause of a disease.

2. A _____ is the sign or symptom of a disease.

3. A _____ code is a single code that identifies both the cause and the signs and symptoms of a disease.

4. The abbreviation NEC stands for _____

_____

_____

and is commonly identified as the "other" option in the ICD-10-CM code book.

5. The abbreviation NOS stands for _____

_____

_____

and is commonly identified as the "unspecified" option in the ICD-10-CM code book.

6. The Index that lists extenuating circumstances surrounding an injury or other medical condition is called the _____.

_____

_____

7. The Index that lists codes that identify toxic effects of chemicals, medicinals, and other substances is called the _____.

_____

_____

8. The Index that lists the majority of medical conditions is called the _____

_____

_____.

9. The _____
lists codes for neoplastic conditions.

10. A(n) _____ modifier in the Index is listed in parentheses and does not impact code selection.

11. A(n) _____ modifier in the Index is listed as a subterm under the main term and does impact code selection.

12. The _____ note in the Tabular List note is a pure Excludes note and indicates that two conditions are mutually exclusive and should not be coded together.

13. The _____ note in the Tabular List identifies conditions "not coded here" and indicates that two conditions should be coded separately if both codes exist.

14. The _____ notes appear directly beneath a three-character category in the Tabular List to further define and give examples of the content that is included within the category.

15. When reporting both acute and chronic conditions, sequence the code for the

_____

_____

condition first.

16. List the four steps for looking up a code in the Main Index.

a. _____

b. _____

c. _____

d. _____

17. When reporting external cause codes, report a code for the

_____

_____

(2 words), which describes the way an injury happened.

18. The _____(3 words) is where the patient was when an injury occurred.

19. The _____ is what the patient was doing when the injury occurred.

20. The _____ (2 words) identifies the patient's work context when the injury occurred.

21. The _____ (2 words) is the structured list of ICD-10-CM codes, organized alphanumerically.

Matching

Instructions: Match the terms with the appropriate descriptions.

1. _____ Index to Diseases and Injury

A. Noncancerous growth of tissue

2. _____ Carcinoma in situ

B. Deliberately acting to injure one's self

3. _____ Benign neoplasm

C. The noun that describes the patient's diagnosis or reason for encounter

4. _____ Subterm

D. Also referred to as a metastasis, this is the site to which a neoplasm has spread

5. _____ Secondary neoplasm

E. Indented under the main term in the Index, gives variations of the main term

6. _____ Main term

F. Unintentional effect as a result of an accident or unintentional overdose

7. _____ Intentional self-harm

G. The main index to the ICD-10-CM code book

8. _____ Assault

H. This cross-reference instructs the coder to look elsewhere for a code

9. _____ _See also_

I. Growth of tissue that can invade other tissues and destroy them

10. _____ Underdosing

J. The original neoplastic growth

11. _____ Malignant neoplasm

K. Unintended effect of a medical substance that has been correctly prescribed and correctly taken

12. _____ Primary neoplasm

L. Neoplastic growth that is potentially cancerous, currently not invasive

13. _____ Accidental intent

M. An act of harm purposefully inflicted upon another person

14. _____ Adverse effect

N. Occurs when a patient takes too little of a prescribed medication

Coding

Instructions: Read the following diagnostic statement and then identify the primary or first-listed diagnosis. Then report the code for the diagnosis.

1. Patient with a long history of shortness of breath and wheezing is diagnosed with moderate persistent asthma.

   a. Primary diagnosis: _____

   b. ICD-10-CM code: _____

2. 34-year-old female presents to the clinic complaining of severe upper right quadrant abdominal pain that is determined to be due to acute cholecystitis.

   a. Primary diagnosis: _____

   b. ICD-10-CM code: _____

3. Patient with sore throat and fever tests negative for streptococcal tonsillitis.

   a. Primary diagnosis: _____

   b. ICD-10-CM code: _____

4. 78-year-old female suffering from confusion presents to the office. Clinician suspects transient ischemic attack.

   a. Primary diagnosis: _____

   b. ICD-10-CM code: _____

Instructions: Report the ICD-10-CM diagnosis code(s) from the following diagnostic statements. Pay attention to sequencing conventions and instructions in the Tabular List to ensure that multiple codes are sequenced correctly.

5. Acute and chronic pancreatitis

   ICD-10-CM code(s): _____, _____

6. Headache

   ICD-10-CM code(s): _____

7. Loefflerella mallei infection

   ICD-10-CM code(s): _____

8. Laceration of the right index finger due to an accident in which patient was cut with a kitchen knife as he was preparing dinner in the kitchen of a single family home while working as a personal chef, initial encounter

   ICD-10-CM code(s) for laceration: _____

   ICD-10-CM code(s) for the injury mechanism: _____

   ICD-10-CM code(s) for the patient activity: _____

   ICD-10-CM code(s) for the place of occurrence: _____

   ICD-10-CM code(s) for the patient status: _____

9. Alligator skin disease

   ICD-10-CM code(s): _____

10. Congenital aplastic anemia (Hint: this is an NEC code)

   ICD-10-CM code(s): _____

11. Black lung disease

   ICD-10-CM code(s): _____

12. Sleep disorder due to sedative abuse

   ICD-10-CM code(s): _____

13. Patient with primary malignant neoplasm of the prostate presents for treatment of neoplasm-related anemia

ICD-10-CM code(s): _____, _____

14. Patient with melanoma of the skin of the back is diagnosed with metastases to the left lung and brain

ICD-10-CM code(s) for the primary neoplasm: _____

ICD-10-CM code(s) for the secondary neoplasms: _____, _____

15. Head lice

ICD-10-CM code(s): _____

16. Meningitis due to Hemophilus influenza

ICD-10-CM code(s): _____

17. Patient presents to the clinic complaining of chest pain upon breathing after breathing in rubbing alcohol fumes, initial encounter (Hint: code for the manifestation of the toxic effect as well as the toxic effect code; look to the beginning of the section for sequencing instructions)

ICD-10-CM code(s): _____, _____

18. Anaphylaxis due to adverse effect of non-steroidal anti-inflammatory drug (NSAID)

ICD-10-CM code(s): _____, _____

19. Subsequent encounter for underdosing of antithrombotic drug

ICD-10-CM code(s): _____

20. Pain in right wrist

ICD-10-CM code(s): _____

21. Patient presents with intestinal obstruction in Crohn's disease of both small and large intestines

ICD-10-CM code(s): _____

22. Acute and chronic prostatitis

ICD-10-CM code(s): _____, _____

23. Hepatic ascites and chronic active hepatitis due to toxic liver disease

ICD-10-CM code(s): _____

24. Unstable angina co-occurrent and due to coronary arteriosclerosis

ICD-10-CM code(s): _____

25. Acute and chronic tonsillitis

ICD-10-CM code(s): _____, _____

Instructions: In each of the following questions, compare the documentation and the code selected. Then identify the component of the diagnosis code missing from the documentation and rewrite the documentation to match the code description.

26. 15-year-old patient presents for a follow-up on her bronchitis. She is feeling better, is less short of breath, and the medications prescribed by the doctor have been helping.

Diagnosis code reported: **J41.0**

Rewrite the documentation to include the detail required in order to support the code reported. _____

_____

_____

27. Patient is seen for a fracture of the right humerus. Fracture was manipulated and immobilized.

Diagnosis code reported: **S42.331A**

Rewrite the documentation to include the detail required in order to support the code reported. _____

_____

_____

28. 62-year-old male presents with superficial foreign body in his finger.

Diagnosis code reported: **S60.451A**

Rewrite the documentation to include the detail required in order to support the code reported. _____

_____

_____

29. 2-year-old female presents for treatment for purulent otitis media.

Diagnosis code selected: **H66.004**

Rewrite the documentation to include the detail required in order to support the code reported. _____

_____

_____

CHAPTER 5

Learning the CPT and HCPCS Code Books

Vocabulary

Instructions: Define each of the following key terms in the space provided.

1. Add-on code: _____

_____

_____

2. Anesthesia section: _____

_____

_____

3. Category I code: _____

_____

_____

4. Category II code: _____

_____

_____

5. Category III code: _____

_____

_____

6. Eponym: _____

_____

_____

7. Evaluation and Management Services section: _____

_____

_____

8. Indented code: _____

_____

_____

9. Medicine section: _____

_____

_____

10. Modifying term: _____

_____

_____

11. Parenthetical note: _____

_____

_____

12. Pathology and Laboratory section: _____

_____

_____

13. Radiology section: _____

_____

_____

14. Resequenced code: _____

_____

_____

15. Separate procedure: _____

_____

_____

16. Special report: _____

_____

_____

17. Standalone code: _____

_____

_____

18. Surgery section: _____

_____

_____

19. Synonym: _____

_____

_____

20. Table of Drugs: _____

_____

_____

21. Telemedicine service: _____

_____

_____

22. Unlisted procedure codes: _____

_____

_____

Fill in the Blank

Instructions: Complete the following statements.

1. Evaluation and management codes are found in the code range
_____.

2. Radiology codes are found in the code range _____.

3. Medicine codes are found in the code range _____.

4. Codes within the 33010 to 37799 range are found in the
_____ subsection of the CPT code book.

5. Codes within the 50010 to 53899 range are found in the
_____ subsection of the CPT code book.

6. Female genital subsection codes in the CPT manual begin with code
_____ and end with code _____.

7. Nervous system subsection codes in the CPT manual begin with code
_____ and end with code _____.

Complete the following figure by labeling the CPT headings.

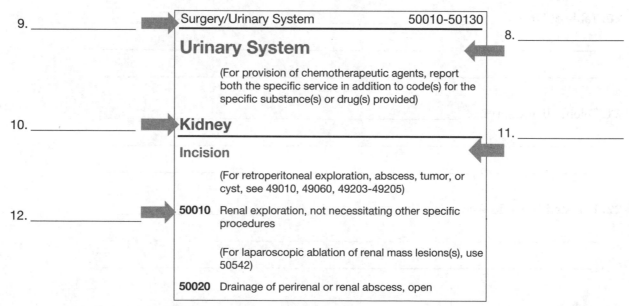

9. _____

10. _____

12. _____

8. _____

11. _____

Surgery/Urinary System   50010-50130

Urinary System

(For provision of chemotherapeutic agents, report both the specific service in addition to code(s) for the specific substance(s) or drug(s) provided)

Kidney

Incision

(For retroperitoneal exploration, abscess, tumor, or cyst, see 49010, 49060, 49203-49205)

50010   Renal exploration, not necessitating other specific procedures

(For laparoscopic ablation of renal mass lesions(s), use 50542)

50020   Drainage of perirenal or renal abscess, open

Source: AMA 2018, 339.

Matching

Instructions: Match the terms with the appropriate descriptions.

1. _____ Category I codes

A. Reports a service in which the provider evaluates and then treats a patient's healthcare needs

2. _____ Category II codes

B. Two digits that alter the meaning of a code, appended to the end of a CPT/HCPCS code

3. _____ Category III codes

C. Set of temporary codes used to report new and emerging technologies

4. _____ Evaluation and Management codes

D. Make up the largest section of codes in the CPT book, describe invasive and noninvasive procedures

5. _____ Anesthesia codes

E. Identify procedures that use radiant energy to diagnose and treat medical conditions

6. _____ Surgery codes

F. Supplemental tracking codes that may be used for performance measurement

7. _____ Radiology codes

G. Identify services provided to reduce pain or alleviate sensation

8. _____ Pathology and Laboratory codes

H. Miscellaneous grouping of codes that represent a vast array of minimally and noninvasive services

9. _____ Medicine codes

I. Divided into subsections, organized by body area or organ system, and describe invasive procedures

10. _____ Modifiers

J. Represent diagnostic tests on human specimens

Instructions: Match the code type with the correct code.

11. _____	HCPCS	**K.**	2060F
12. _____	ICD-10-CM	**L.**	0NTV0ZZ
13. _____	ICD-10-PCS	**M.**	K0890
14. _____	CPT	**N.**	M86.479
15. _____	Category II CPT	**O.**	59610
16. _____	Category III CPT	**P.**	0209T

Coding

Instructions: Report the CPT or HCPCS code(s) from the following statements.

1. Evisceration of ocular contents of the left eye, without subsequent implantation of prosthetic eye

CPT code(s): _____

2. Ventriculocisternostomy of the third ventricle

CPT code(s): _____

3. Total thymectomy via transcervical approach

CPT code(s): _____

4. Computed tomography of the brain without contrast

CPT code(s): _____

5. Fluorescein angioscopy with interpretation and report

CPT code(s): _____

6. Tobacco use assessed performed as part of preventive care performance measurement

CPT code(s): _____

7. Automated speech audiometry threshold

CPT code(s): _____

8. Needle biopsy of salivary gland

CPT code(s): _____

9. Abrasion of 5 keratotic lesions

CPT code(s): _____, _____

10. Proetz therapy of the nose

CPT code(s): _____

11. Level 3 Molecular pathology procedure

CPT code(s): _____

12. Unlisted procedure of urinary system

CPT code(s): _____

13. Excision of bulbourethral gland

CPT code(s): _____

14. Prophylactic pinning of clavicle

CPT code(s): _____

15. Male to female intersex surgery

CPT code(s): _____

16. 3 patch allergy tests

CPT code(s): _____ × _____

17. SPECT brain imaging

CPT code(s): _____

18. Floating kyphosis pad

HCPCS code(s): _____

19. Alcohol misuse screening

HCPCS code(s): _____

20. Tracheostomy tube collar

HCPCS code(s): _____

21. 1 mg Clolar (Hint: this is a medication administered in the healthcare setting)

HCPCS code(s): _____

22. Amygdalin

HCPCS code(s): _____

23. Injection of 20 units of Taliglucerace alfa

HCPCS code(s): _____ × _____

24. Wig

HCPCS code(s): _____

25. Heat lamp with stand and infrared element

HCPCS code(s): _____

26. Barium enema colorectal cancer screening

HCPCS code(s): _____

27. 5 units of irradiated platelets

HCPCS code(s): _____ × _____

Reference

American Medical Association. 2018. Current Procedural Terminology: 2018 Professional Edition. Chicago: AMA.

Part II

Coding
In the Real World

CHAPTER

Supplies and Services

Vocabulary

Instructions: Define each of the following key terms in the space provided.

1. Advanced life support (ALS): _____

_____

_____

2. Ambulance modifier: _____

_____

_____

3. Ambulance supplier: _____

_____

_____

4. Basic life support (BLS): _____

_____

_____

5. Certificate of Medical Necessity (CMN): _____

_____

_____

6. Destination: _____

_____

_____

7. Durable medical equipment (DME): _____

_____

_____

8. Durable medical equipment, prosthetics, orthotics, and supplies (DMEPOS): ___

_____

_____

9. Emergency transportation: _____

_____

_____

10. Nonemergency transportation: _____

_____

_____

11. Non-ambulatory: _____

_____

_____

12. Origin: _____

_____

_____

13. Orthotics: _____

_____

_____

14. Physician's Desk Reference (PDR): _____

_____

_____

15. Prosthetics: _____

_____

_____

16. Route of administration: _____

_____

_____

17. Supplies: _____

_____

_____

18. Services _____

_____

_____

19. Transportation indicator: _____

_____

_____

Matching

Instructions: Match the terms with the appropriate acronyms.

1. _____ IV   **A.** Intra-arterial

2. _____ VAR   **B.** Intravenous

3. _____ IA   **C.** Intramuscular

4. _____ ORAL   **D.** Intrathecal

5. _____ SC   **E.** Subcutaneous

6. _____ OTH   **F.** Inhaled

7. _____ INH   **G.** Various routes

8. _____ IT   **H.** Other routes

9. _____ IM   **I.** Oral

True/False

Instructions: Indicate whether the following statements are true or false (T or F). For false statements, rewrite the statement on the line below to make the statement true.

1. HCPCS Level II codes are used to report ambulance services.

_____

_____

2. The type of life support services provided during the ambulance services does not make a difference in code selection.

_____

_____

3. The type of vehicle used in ambulance transportation does not make a difference in code selection.

_____

_____

4. Transportation indicators are used to specify the type of supply provided for DME claims.

_____

_____

5. Medical necessity does not play a role in DMEPOS billing.

_____

_____

6. A certificate of medical necessity is used to indicate that a DME item is medically necessary.

_____

_____

7. When coding for drugs administered in the medical setting, the route of administration may impact code selection.

_____

_____

8. Drugs administered in the medical setting are identified with CPT level II codes.

_____

_____

9. If more than one HCPCS code exists for a specific drug, code selection will depend on the route of administration or unit per dose.

_____

_____

10. The majority of the codes used to identify drugs administered in the medical setting begin with the letter J.

_____

_____

Coding

Instructions: Answer the question with the appropriate HCPCS, ICD-10, modifier, or transportation indicator code.

1. Ambulance service ground mileage for 15 miles (include only the mileage code).

HCPCS code: _____ × _____

2. Nonemergency taxi transportation.

HCPCS code: _____

3. Fixed wing air transportation, 43 miles traveled.

HCPCS code: _____

HCPCS code: _____ × _____

4. Ambulance was dispatched to the scene of an accident, but no injuries were encountered on the scene. Code for the ambulance response with no transport provided.

HCPCS code: _____

5. What transportation indicator would be used for an air transportation service that was provided due to a factory explosion?

Transportation indicator: _____

6. Ground ambulance dispatched to the scene of an accident. Woman at the scene had severe laceration of her upper right thigh area. She was transported via emergency ALS ambulance van to an acute-care hospital, 9 miles total.

HCPCS code: _____ - _____

HCPCS code: _____ × _____

ICD-10 code: _____

7. Level 1 ALS ambulance transported a woman complaining of shortness of breath and chest pains to an acute-care hospital, Level 1 emergency ALS transport, 12 miles total.

HCPCS code: _____ - _____

HCPCS code: _____ × _____

ICD-10 code: _____, _____

8. Pediatric patient with ESRD transferred via nonemergency ALS level 1 transport to location 236 miles away. Patient was transferred to another facility due to the nature of his medical needs, he requires specialized services not available in the local area.

HCPCS code: _____

HCPCS code: _____ × _____

Transportation indicator: _____

ICD-10 code: _____

Enter these codes in the correct spaces on the following CMS-1500 claim form. Enter only the HCPCS codes (with units), transportation indicator (in box 19), and ICD-10 codes on the form.

19. ADDITIONAL CLAIM INFORMATION (Designated by NUCC)									20. OUTSIDE LAB? ☐ YES ☐ NO	

21. DIAGNOSIS OR NATURE OF ILLNESS OR INJURY Relate A-L to service line below (24E)				ICD Ind.		22. RESUBMISSION CODE	
A. ⌐⎯⎯⎯⎯	B. ⌐⎯⎯⎯⎯	C. ⌐⎯⎯⎯⎯	D. ⌐⎯⎯⎯⎯				
E. ⌐⎯⎯⎯⎯	F. ⌐⎯⎯⎯⎯	G. ⌐⎯⎯⎯⎯	H. ⌐⎯⎯⎯⎯			23. PRIOR AUTHORIZATION NU	
I. ⌐⎯⎯⎯⎯	J. ⌐⎯⎯⎯⎯	K. ⌐⎯⎯⎯⎯	L. ⌐⎯⎯⎯⎯				

24. A.	DATE(S) OF SERVICE						B. PLACE OF SERVICE	C. EMG	D. PROCEDURES, SERVICES, OR SUPPLIES (Explain Unusual Circumstances) CPT/HCPCS | MODIFIER	E. DIAGNOSIS POINTER	F. $ CHARGES	G. DAYS OR UNITS
	From MM	DD	YY	To MM	DD	YY						
1												
2												
3												
4												
5												
6												

9. Woman presents to the office of her OBGYN for the fitting of a diaphragm. Her provider counsels her on contraception and family planning and provides her with the diaphragm. (Code only for the HCPCS supply and ICD-10, not the CPT code for the service.)

    HCPCS code: _____

    ICD-10 code: _____

10. Custom fabricated plastic AFO provided to a patient with a healed complete traumatic right lower leg amputation. (Hint: because the patient is not undergoing any active treatment at this time, use the seventh character extension for subsequent encounter.)

    HCPCS code: _____

    ICD-10 code: _____

11. Blood glucose monitor with integrated voice synthesizer for patient with uncomplicated diabetes mellitus type II.

    HCPCS code: _____

    ICD-10 code: _____

12. Pediatric size wheelchair with tilt-in-space, folding, adjustable, with seating system.

    HCPCS code: _____

13. CPAP device provided to 43-year-old male with obstructive sleep apnea. Additional length of CPAP tubing also provided.

    HCPCS code: _____

    HCPCS code: _____

    ICD-10 code: _____

14. Patient provided with nutritionally incomplete enteral formula (Propac), administered through feeding tube. 500 calories total.

    HCPCS code: _____ × _____

15. Rigid, wheeled, adjustable height walker provided to Medicare patient with ataxic gait.

    HCPCS code: _____

    ICD-10 code: _____

16. 10 mg IV Haldol.

    HCPCS code: _____ x _____

17. Patient provided with 200 mg of ciprofloxacin for intravenous infusion.

    HCPCS code: _____

18. 30 mCi therapeutic dose of IV 20 Zevalin.

HCPCS code: _____

19. 20 units subcutaneous Vasopressin.

HCPCS code: _____

20. 2 units incobotulinumtoxinA administered intramuscularly to 43-year-old female with glabellar lines.

HCPCS code: _____ × _____

21. 5 sq. cm Integra Matrix provided to patient with diabetic (non-ressure) ulcer on left heel.

HCPCS code: _____ × _____

ICD-10 code: _____

22. Pentate Zinc Trisodium (25 ml per study dose), intravenous form.

HCPCS code: _____

23. 50 mg oral Etoposide.

HCPCS code: _____

24. 25 mg Folex PFS.

HCPCS code: _____ × _____

25. A Medicare patient was provided with an electric, separate seat lift mechanism for use with her own furniture. Complete the following CMS-849 Certificate of Medical Necessity form for this patient, using the following information.

Section A:

Patient Information: Sally B. Good, 1234 Pleasant Road, Pleasantville, TX, 12345. (555)987-6543. DOB: 02/17/1965. Female. 5′ 1.5″ tall.

Supplier Name: National Medical Equipment and Supplies, 12345 Medical Lane, Pleasantville, TX. 12345. (555) 576-8542. NPI # 123456789

Name and address and facility: not applicable

Supply Item/Service Requested: HCPCS code: _____

Section C: Provide a narrative description of the supply requested

DEPARTMENT OF HEALTH AND HUMAN SERVICES
CENTERS FOR MEDICARE & MEDICAID SERVICES

Form Approved
OMB No. 0938-0679

CERTIFICATE OF MEDICAL NECESSITY
CMS-849 — SEAT LIFT MECHANISMS

DME 07.03A

SECTION A: Certification Type/Date: INITIAL ___/___/___ REVISED ___/___/___ RECERTIFICATION___/___/___

PATIENT NAME, ADDRESS, TELEPHONE and HICN	SUPPLIER NAME, ADDRESS, TELEPHONE and NSC or NPI #
(_ _ _) _ _ _ - _ _ _ _ HICN _____	(_ _ _) _ _ _ - _ _ _ _ NSC or NPI #_____

PLACE OF SERVICE _____	Supply Item/Service Procedure Code(s):	PT DOB ___/___/___ Sex ___ (M/F) Ht. ___(in) Wt ___
NAME and ADDRESS of FACILITY *if applicable (see reverse)*	_____ _____ _____ _____	PHYSICIAN NAME, ADDRESS, TELEPHONE and UPIN or NPI # (_ _ _) _ _ _ - _ _ _ _ UPIN or NPI #_____

SECTION B: Information in this Section May Not Be Completed by the Supplier of the Items/Supplies.

EST. LENGTH OF NEED (# OF MONTHS): _____ 1-99 *(99=LIFETIME)*	DIAGNOSIS CODES: _____ _____ _____ _____

ANSWERS	ANSWER QUESTIONS 1-5 FOR SEAT LIFT MECHANISM (Check Y for Yes, N for No, or D for Does Not Apply)
❏ Y ❏ N ❏ D	1. Does the patient have severe arthritis of the hip or knee?
❏ Y ❏ N ❏ D	2. Does the patient have a severe neuromuscular disease?
❏ Y ❏ N ❏ D	3. Is the patient completely incapable of standing up from a regular armchair or any chair in his/her home?
❏ Y ❏ N ❏ D	4. Once standing, does the patient have the ability to ambulate?
❏ Y ❏ N ❏ D	5. Have all appropriate therapeutic modalities to enable the patient to transfer from a chair to a standing position (e.g., medication, physical therapy) been tried and failed? If YES, this is documented in the patient's medical records.

NAME OF PERSON ANSWERING SECTION B QUESTIONS, IF OTHER THAN PHYSICIAN (Please Print):
NAME: _____ TITLE: _____ EMPLOYER:_____

SECTION C: Narrative Description of Equipment and Cost

(1) Narrative description of all items, accessories and options ordered; (2) Supplier's charge; and (3) Medicare Fee Schedule Allowance for each item, accessory, and option. (see instructions on back)

SECTION D: PHYSICIAN Attestation and Signature/Date

I certify that I am the treating physician identified in Section A of this form. I have received Sections A, B and C of the Certificate of Medical Necessity (including charges for items ordered). Any statement on my letterhead attached hereto, has been reviewed and signed by me. I certify that the medical necessity information in Section B is true, accurate and complete, to the best of my knowledge, and I understand that any falsification, omission, or concealment of material fact in that section may subject me to civil or criminal liability.

PHYSICIAN'S SIGNATURE_____ DATE ____/____/____
Signature and Date Stamps Are Not Acceptable.

Form CMS-849 (11/11)
Source: CMS 2005.

References

Centers for Medicare and Medicaid Services. 2017. Details for title: CMS 1500. https://www.cms .gov/Medicare/CMS-Forms/CMS-Forms/CMS-Forms-Items/CMS1188854.html.

Centers for Medicare and Medicaid Services. 2005. Details for title: CMS 849. https://www.cms .gov/Medicare/CMS-Forms/CMS-Forms/CMS-Forms-Items/CMS006687.html.

CHAPTER 7

Behavioral Health Services

Vocabulary

Instructions: Define each of the following key terms in the space provided.

1. Anxiety disorders: _____

_____

_____

2. Attention-deficit hyperactivity disorder: _____

_____

_____

3. Behavioral health services: _____

_____

_____

4. Bipolar disorder: _____

_____

_____

5. Contributory factors: _____

_____

_____

6. Coordination of care: _____

_____

_____

7. Counseling: _____

_____

_____

8. Depression: _____

_____

_____

9. Diagnostic and Statistical Manual of Mental Disorders (DSM-5): _____

_____

_____

10. Eating disorders: _____

_____

_____

11. Electroconvulsive therapy (ECT): _____

_____

_____

12. Established patient: _____

_____

_____

13. Examination: _____

_____

_____

14. History: _____

_____

_____

15. Inpatient: _____

_____

_____

16. Interactive complexity: _____

_____

_____

17. Medical decision making (MDM): _____

_____

_____

18. Mental health: _____

_____

_____

19. Mental illness: _____

_____

_____

20. Narcosynthesis for psychiatric purposes: _____

_____

_____

21. Nature of the presenting problem: _____

_____

_____

22. New patient: _____

_____

_____

23. Outpatient: _____

_____

_____

24. Partial hospitalization: _____

_____

_____

25. Place of service (POS): _____

_____

_____

26. Psychotherapy: _____

_____

_____

27. Schizophrenia: _____

_____

_____

28. Screening, Brief Intervention and Referral to Treatment (SBIRT): _____

_____

_____

29. Substance abuse: _____

_____

_____

30. Transcranial magnetic stimulation (TMS): _____

_____

_____

31. Vagus nerve stimulation: _____

_____

_____

Multiple Choice

Instructions: Choose the best answer.

1. Which of the following specialties focuses specifically on the misuse of alcohol or drugs?
   a. Substance abuse
   b. Mental health
   c. Behavioral health
   d. Psychology

2. Which of the following is a type of mid-level provider that may provide behavioral health services?
   a. Medical Doctor (MD)
   b. Doctor of Osteopathy (DO)
   c. Medical Assistant (MA)
   d. Clinical Psychologist (CP)

3. What is the term for the two-digit code that identifies the setting in which the service was provided?
   a. Modifier
   b. Place of service code
   c. Transportation indicator
   d. HCPCS modifier

4. A new patient is a patient who has not received any professional services from the same provider or another provider of the same specialty and subspecialty in the same group practice in how many years?
   a. Two
   b. Three
   c. Four
   d. Five

5. An established patient is one who has received professional services from the same provider or another provider of the same specialty and subspecialty in the same group practice in how many years?
   a. Two
   b. Three
   c. Four
   d. Five

6. Which of the following types of patients has been formally admitted to a healthcare facility?
   a. Inpatient
   b. Outpatient
   c. Observation
   d. Established

7. Which of the following key components is the subjective information (given by the patient)?
  a. History
  b. Examination
  c. Counseling
  d. Coordination of care

8. Which of the following key components is the objective information (as determined by the healthcare provider)?
  a. Examination
  b. Time
  c. Medical decision making
  d. Nature of the presenting problem

9. Which of the following key components involves the provider's determination of the patient's diagnoses and a course of treatment?
  a. Examination
  b. Medical decision making
  c. Coordination of care
  d. History

10. Which of the following contributory factors identifies the type of condition for which the patient is receiving treatment?
  a. Coordination of care
  b. Counseling
  c. Nature of presenting problem
  d. Time

11. In order to select time as the determining factor in the level of an E/M code, what percentage of time must be spent on counseling or coordination of care?
  a. 30%
  b. 45%
  c. 100%
  d. 50%

12. Which of the following are the most commonly used behavioral health procedure codes (besides E/M service codes)?
  a. Narcosynthesis
  b. Transcranial magnetic stimulation (TMS)
  c. Psychotherapy
  d. Vagus nerve stimulation

13. When a medical E/M and psychotherapy are provided at the same encounter, how is the psychotherapy coded?
  a. It is not coded; it is bundled into the code for the E/M service.
  b. It is reported only with the medical E/M code.
  c. It is reported with the psychotherapy add-on code.
  d. It is reported with the psychotherapy standalone code.

14. When a behavioral health service is provided via a telemedicine platform, what modifier should be used?

    a. -95

    b. -59

    c. -51

    d. -25

15. If abuse and dependence are both documented for a single substance, what should the coder do?

    a. Assign the diagnosis codes for both.

    b. Assign the diagnosis code for the abuse only.

    c. Assign the diagnosis code for the dependence only.

    d. Assign the diagnosis code that combines the two conditions.

Fill in the Blank

Instructions: Complete each figure with the levels of each of the key components, in order from lowest to highest.

1. Levels of key component: History

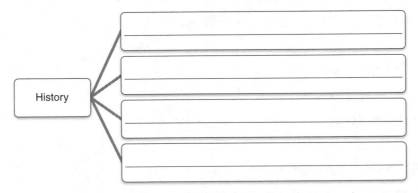

2. Levels of key component: Examination

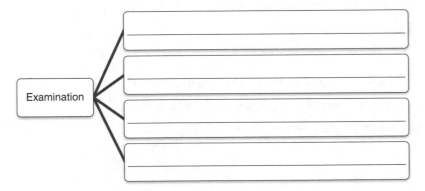

3. Levels of key component: Medical Decision Making

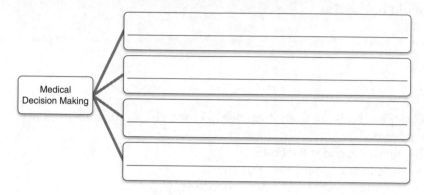

4. Anatomy of an E/M code

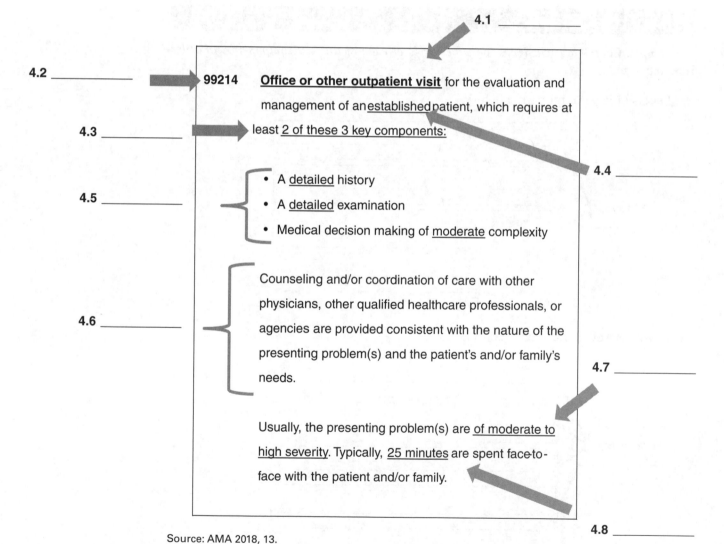

4.1 _____

4.2 _____

4.3 _____

99214   **Office or other outpatient visit** for the evaluation and management of an established patient, which requires at least 2 of these 3 key components:

4.4 _____

4.5 _____

• A detailed history

• A detailed examination

• Medical decision making of moderate complexity

4.6 _____

Counseling and/or coordination of care with other physicians, other qualified healthcare professionals, or agencies are provided consistent with the nature of the presenting problem(s) and the patient's and/or family's needs.

4.7 _____

Usually, the presenting problem(s) are of moderate to high severity. Typically, 25 minutes are spent face-to-face with the patient and/or family.

4.8 _____

Source: AMA 2018, 13.

Coding

Instructions: Answer the question with the appropriate CPT and ICD-10-CM code(s).

1. Factitious disorder with predominantly physical signs.

   ICD-10-CM code(s): _____

2. Patient with Down syndrome (trisomy 21 translocation) and severe intellectual disabilities (patient has a measured IQ of 40).

   ICD-10-CM code(s): _____ , _____

3. Sexual sadism.

   ICD-10-CM code(s): _____

4. ADHD in 32-year-old male.

   ICD-10-CM code(s): _____

5. Post-concussion encephalopathy with intractable post-traumatic headache.

   ICD-10-CM code(s): _____ , _____

6. 50 minutes of family psychotherapy without patient present, delivered via interactive telemedicine portal.

   CPT code(s): _____ - _____

7. Two hours (120 minutes) of psychotherapy for crisis.

   CPT code(s): _____ , _____ × _____

8. Unlisted psychiatric service.

   CPT code(s): _____

9. Diagnostic psychiatry evaluation with interactive complexity.

   CPT code(s): _____ , _____

10. E/M of an established 7-year-old patient in the outpatient office with selective mutism, which involved a detailed history, problem-focused examination, and MDM of moderate complexity.

   CPT code(s): _____

   ICD-10-CM code(s): _____

11. E/M for a new patient in the outpatient office with phobic issues. Male is 45 years old and is scared to leave the house, open the blinds, and generally fearful of other people and answering the door. After a comprehensive history, a detailed examination and MDM of moderate complexity, patient was diagnosed with agoraphobia without panic disorder.

    CPT code(s): _____

    ICD-10-CM code(s): _____

12. Consultation for an inpatient with suicidal ideation. E/M involved a detailed history, a detailed examination, and MDM of low complexity.

    CPT code(s): _____

    ICD-10-CM code(s): _____

13. Psychiatric diagnostic evaluation for a patient with patient with heroin (opioid) dependence, with heroin-induced psychotic disorder. Patient has been experiencing auditory and visual hallucinations.

    CPT code(s): _____

    ICD-10-CM code(s): _____

14. Code for the evaluation and management of an established patient with unspecified depression. Detailed history, expanded problem-focused examination, and low complexity MDM.

    CPT code(s): _____

    ICD-10-CM code(s): _____

15. On-call psychiatrist was called in to emergency department to treat a 23-year-old female with severe panic attack. Patient also has a history of bipolar disorder. E/M service (which included a detailed history, a detailed examination, and moderate complexity MDM) led to a clinical diagnosis of: bipolar disorder with current moderate manic episode; panic attack.

    CPT code(s): _____

    ICD-10-CM code(s): _____ , _____

16. Medical E/M of established patient with paranoid schizophrenia (expanded problem-focused history and examination, low complexity MDM), along with 30 minutes of psychotherapy.

    CPT code(s): _____ , _____

    ICD-10-CM code(s): _____

17. 8 minutes of tobacco cessation counseling for a 37-year-old male current cigarette smoker (dependent on approx. 1.5 pack per day).

    CPT code(s): _____

    ICD-10-CM code(s): _____

18. Electroconvulsive therapy (ECT) for severe recurrent major depressive disorder with psychotic features.

CPT code(s): _____

ICD-10-CM code(s): _____

19. Psychoanalysis of patient with oppositional defiant disorder.

CPT code(s): _____

ICD-10-CM code(s): _____

Reference

American Medical Association. 2018. Current Procedural Terminology: 2018 Professional Edition. Chicago: AMA.

CHAPTER 8

Primary Care Services

Vocabulary

Instructions: Define each of the following key terms in the space provided.

1. Body area: _____

_____

_____

2. Chief complaint (C/C): _____

_____

_____

3. Chronic obstructive pulmonary disease (COPD): _____

_____

_____

4. CLIA-waived: _____

_____

_____

5. Diabetes mellitus: _____

_____

_____

6. Electrocardiogram (ECG/EKG): _____

_____

_____

7. Foreign body: _____

_____

_____

8. Heart failure: _____

_____

_____

9. History of present illness (HPI): _____

_____

_____

10. Hypercholesterolemia: _____

_____

_____

11. Hyperlipidemia: _____

_____

_____

12. Hypertension: _____

_____

_____

13. Immune globulin: _____

_____

_____

14. Incision and drainage (I&D): _____

_____

_____

15. Minor surgical procedure: _____

_____

_____

16. Organ system: _____

_____

_____

17. Otitis: _____

_____

_____

18. Overcoding: _____

_____

_____

19. Past, family, social history (PFSH): _____

_____

_____

20. Preventive medicine services: _____

_____

_____

21. Primary care: _____

_____

_____

22. Primary care provider (PCP): _____

_____

_____

23. Review of systems (ROS): _____

_____

_____

24. Status asthmaticus: _____

_____

_____

25. Undercoding: _____

_____

_____

26. Underdose: _____

_____

_____

27. Vaccine administration: _____

_____

_____

28. Vaccine toxoid: _____

_____

_____

Multiple Choice

Instructions: Choose the best answer.

1. Which of the following types of codes are the most commonly reported procedures in primary care?
a. Evaluation and management
b. Medicine procedures
c. Vaccinations
d. In-office procedures

2. How many key components are there to E/M codes?
a. Two
b. Three
c. Four
d. Five

3. Which of the following is not an element of the key component of history?
a. Chief complaint
b. Risk of complications or morbidity or mortality
c. History of present illness
d. Review of systems

4. Which of the following elements of history is the patient's description of his or her reason for encounter?

a. Chief complaint

b. History of present illness

c. Review of systems

d. Past, family, social history

5. In the history of present illness, the characteristics of the sign(s) or symptom(s) are which of the following?

a. Location

b. Severity

c. Context

d. Quality

6. Which of the following elements of the key component history is aimed at obtaining more information regarding the patient's signs or symptoms?

a. Examination

b. History of present illness

c. Review of systems

d. Associated signs and symptoms

7. Which of the following elements of MDM considers the relative danger that a medical condition can pose to the patient if left untreated?

a. Risk of complications, morbidity, or mortality

b. Number of diagnoses and management options

c. Amount and/or complexity of data

d. Review of present illness

8. Which of the following modifiers may not be used with an E/M service?

a. Modifier -25

b. Modifier -32

c. Modifier -59

d. Modifier -57

9. There are two components to vaccine coding, the administration of the vaccine and which of the following?

a. Vaccine order

b. Immunoglobulin

c. Toxic substance

d. Toxoid or serum

10. Which of the following is a chronic lung disease characterized by chronically poor airflow?

a. Asthma

b. COPD

c. DM

d. Hypertension

Completion

Instructions: Define each of the following elements of history of present illness (HPI) and give an example of each.

1. Location: _____

　　Example: _____

2. Quality: _____

　　Example: _____

3. Severity: _____

　　Example: _____

4. Duration: _____

　　Example: _____

5. Timing: _____

　　Example: _____

6. Context: _____

　　Example: _____

7. Modifying factors: _____

　　Example: _____

8. Associated signs and symptoms: _____

　　Example: _____

Instructions: List and define the 14 elements (body systems) included in the review of systems.

9. _____

10. _____

11. _____

12. _____

13. _____

14. _____

15. _____

16. _____

17. _____

18. _____

19. _____

20. _____

21. _____

22. _____

Coding

Instructions: Read the documentation of the following E/M service and determine the levels of each of the elements.

C/C: Swollen tonsils, congestion, fever, and nausea

HPI: Patient began experiencing swollen tonsils, congestion, and fever two days ago. Also experiencing dizziness, hot flashes, and vomiting for two weeks. Hot flashes seem to happen when she goes to bed at night and when she wakes up in the morning. Nausea only happens after meals. She's been taking aspirin for the fever.

ROS: Constitutional:reports having fever for the last two days

Eyes:negative findings

Respiratory:negative

Cardiovascular:patient reports no problems

Gastrointestinal:patient reports nausea and vomiting

Neurological:patient reports dizziness and vertigo

Integumentary:negative finding

HENT:reports symptoms of throat problems congestion

Endocrine:negative findings

Musculoskeletal:negative findings

Psychiatric:negative findings

Genitourinary:reports having scanty and/or late menses

PFSH: Allergic to hydrocodone, no family history of early menopause

---

Coding continued on next page

(Continued)

1. What is the level of HPI for this encounter?

_____

_____

2. What is the level of ROS for this encounter?

_____

_____

3. What is the level of PFSH for this encounter?

_____

_____

4. Using the following table, determine the level of history for this encounter (remember that all three of the three elements must meet or exceed the same level).

_____

_____

Level of History	HPI	ROS	PFSH
Problem focused	Brief	N/A	N/A
Expanded problem focused	Brief	Problem pertinent	N/A
Detailed	Extended	Extended	Pertinent
Comprehensive	Extended	Complete	Complete

Source: Table 8.1, p. 217.

EXAMINATION:

BMI 25.4   BP: 98/64   H: 59.00 in   P: 90/min   RR: 20/min   T: 99.1 F   W: 125lbs 6oz

Gen: general appearance fine, seems tired

HEENT: oropharynx red/erythematous, NOSE: positive erythema

NECK: n/a

LUNGS: Respiration within normal limits (wnl)

CHEST/BREASTS: n/a

HEART: wnl

ABD: wnl

GENT: wnl, pelvic examination deferred

MUSC: wnl

NEURO: wnl

SKIN: wnl

STUDIES: none

5. Using the 1997 guidelines and the following table, determine the level of examination for this encounter.

_____

_____

Level of Exam	Exam Components	Number of Body Areas/Organ Systems: 1995 Guidelines	Number of Body Areas/Organ Systems: 1997 Guidelines
Problem focused	Limited exam of affected body area/organ system	1 body area or organ system	1 to 5 body areas or organ systems
Expanded problem focused	Limited exam of affected area and other related/symptomatic organ systems	2 to 7 body areas or organ systems	6 to 11 body areas or organ systems
Detailed	Extended exam of affected area and other related/symptomatic organ systems	Extended exam of 2 to 7 body areas or organ systems	2 areas of examination from 6 organ systems
Comprehensive	General multisystem exam or complete exam of single organ system	8 or more organ systems	2 areas of examination from 9 organ systems

Source: Table 8.4, p. 220.

ASSESSMENT:	Irregular menses (ICD-10 N92.6)
	Dizziness (ICD-10 R42)
	Acute Upper Respiratory Infection (J06.9)
	Acute Pharyngitis (J02.9)
	Vomiting (R11.10)
PLAN:	Strep swab in office (negative)
	Continue with aspirin to treat fever
	Return if symptoms worsen
	HCG pregnancy two weeks ago at home was negative

6. Using the following table, determine the number of diagnoses or treatment options for this encounter.

_____

_____

Number of Diagnoses and Management Options	Points
Minor problem (self-resolving)	1 each for a maximum of 2
Established (stable or improving)	1 each
Established (worsening)	2 each
New problem (no additional workup)	3
New problem (with additional workup)	4
Total	

Source: Table 8.4, p. 225.

7. Using the following table, determine the amount and/or complexity of data to be reviewed.

_____

_____

Amount and/or Complexity of Data	Points
Lab ordered or reviewed	1 maximum
Radiologic exam ordered or reviewed	1 maximum
Medicine section test ordered or reviewed	1 each
Discussion of results with performing provider	1
Decision to obtain old records or history	1
Reviewing and summarizing old records, history, or discussion with other health provider	2
Independent interpretation of test results	2
Total	

Source: Table 8.4, p. 225.

8. Determine the risk of complications and/or morbidity or mortality for this encounter.

_____

_____

9. Using the following table, determine the level of MDM for this encounter.

_____

_____

Level of MDM	Number of Diagnosis or Management Options	Amount and/or Complexity of Data	Risk Involved
Straightforward	Minimal	Minimal or none	Minimal
Low	Limited	Limited	Low
Moderate	Multiple	Moderate	Moderate
High	Extensive	Extensive	High

Source: Table 8.4, p. 227.

10. Using the levels of history, examination, and medical decision making determined previously, report the code for this outpatient office encounter for an established patient.

CPT code(s): _____

Instructions: Assign the correct CPT and ICD-10-CM codes for the following.

11. Type 1 patient with diabetes mellitus presents for evaluation of her long-term insulin regimen.

ICD-10-CM code(s): _____

12. Underdosing of insulin in patient with type 1 DM due to mechanical breakdown of pump. Patient has been experiencing hyperglycemia.

ICD-10-CM code(s): _____, _____

13. Patient with uncontrolled type 2 DM and long-term use of insulin presents for treatment of diabetic ulcer of left heel ulcer (limited to breakdown of skin).

ICD-10-CM code(s): _____, _____

14. Administration of MMR vaccine to 4-year-old patient, with counseling.

CPT code(s): _____, _____, _____,
_____

ICD-10-CM code(s): _____

15. 48-year-old established male patient with COPD and moderate persistent asthma presents for exacerbation of both chronic conditions. Detailed history and examination with moderate complexity MDM.

CPT code(s): _____, _____, _____
ICD-10-CM code(s): _____

16. An outpatient office visit for an established 15-year-old male with moderate persistent asthma with status asthmaticus required a detailed history and examination, with MDM of moderate complexity. Patient was also provided with a pressurized breathing treatment in the office and an additional 35 minutes of time was spent monitoring the patient before he was sent home. Total time spent during this prolonged encounter was 55 minutes.

CPT code(s): _____, _____, _____
ICD-10-CM code(s): _____

17. 63-year-old male established patient presented to the office of his PCP for routine examination, no abnormal findings.

CPT code(s): _____
ICD-10-CM code(s): _____

18. 31-year-old pregnant female received IM annual flu vaccine (trivalent IIV3 0.5 mL dosage) as well as Tdap booster shots.

CPT code(s): _____, _____, _____,
_____

ICD-10-CM code(s): _____

19. HCG urinalysis performed on 25-year-old female patient complaining of amenorrhea.

CPT code(s): _____

ICD-10-CM code(s): _____

20. Routine physical examination performed on a 50-year-old new male patient with uncontrolled type 2 DM and essential hypertension. Patient has a family history of cardiovascular disease and his current BMI is 32.3. Intranasal flu vaccine administered upon request.

CPT code(s): _____, _____, _____

ICD-10-CM code(s): _____, _____,

_____, _____, _____, _____

21. Outpatient office visit for established 54-year-old male with a history of smoking and COPD. Currently experiencing acute bronchitis and exacerbation of COPD. Comprehensive examination and high complexity MDM.

CPT code(s): _____

ICD-10-CM code(s): _____, _____, _____,

_____

CHAPTER

Eye and Vision Services

Vocabulary

Instructions: Define each of the following key terms in the space provided.

1. Acquired condition: _____

_____

_____

2. Congenital condition: _____

_____

_____

_____

3. Comprehensive ophthalmological services: _____

_____

_____

4. Cortical cataract: _____

_____

_____

5. Enucleation: _____

_____

_____

6. Evisceration: _____

_____

_____

7. Exenteration: _____

_____

_____

8. Extracapsular cataract extraction (ECCE): _____

_____

_____

9. Glaucoma: _____

_____

_____

10. Goniolens: _____

_____

_____

11. Intermediate ophthalmological services: _____

_____

_____

12. Intracapsular cataract extraction (ICCE): _____

_____

_____

13. Intraocular pressure: _____

_____

_____

14. Lifestyle impairments: _____

_____

_____

15. Macular degeneration: _____

_____

_____

16. Nuclear cataract: _____

_____

_____

17. Ocular adnexa: _____

_____

_____

18. Ophthalmologist: _____

_____

_____

19. Ophthalmology: _____

_____

_____

20. Optometrist: _____

_____

_____

21. Optometry: _____

_____

_____

22. Phacoemulsification: _____

_____

_____

23. Refraction: _____

_____

_____

24. Refractive surgery: _____

_____

_____

25. Retinal detachment: _____

_____

_____

26. Slit lamp: _____

_____

_____

27. Strabismus: _____

_____

_____

28. Subcapsular cataract: _____

_____

_____

29. Trabeculectomy: _____

_____

_____

30. Vision insurance: _____

_____

_____

Multiple Choice

Instructions: Choose the best answer.

1. Which of the following types of insurance covers routine eye wellness exams, contact lens fitting, and hardware and corrective lenses?
a. Behavioral health insurance
b. Health insurance
c. Vision insurance
d. Dental insurance

2. Which of the following services would be covered by health insurance rather than vision insurance?

a. Diagnostic screenings

b. Refraction

c. Injuries of the eye

d. Contact lens fitting

3. Which of the following includes the accessory structure of the eye, including the extraocular muscles, eyelids, and lacrimal system?

a. Ocular adnexa

b. Anterior segment

c. Extrinsic eye muscles

d. Posterior segment

4. Which of the following codes would be used to report an intermediate ophthalmological service provided to a new patient?

a. 92004

b. 92012

c. 92014

d. 92002

5. Which of the following codes would be used to report a comprehensive ophthalmological service provided to an established patient?

a. 92002

b. 92004

c. 92012

d. 92014

6. Which of the following types of codes would be used to report the supply provided to patients for corrective lenses?

a. HCPCS

b. CPT

c. ICD-10-CM

d. None, these items are not reported separately

7. Which of the following types of surgeries are performed to reshape the cornea and improve eye sight?

a. Trabeculectomy

b. Refractive surgeries

c. Gonioscopy

d. Goniotomy

8. Which of the following types of glaucoma is due to a narrow angle between the iris and cornea?

a. Open-angle

b. Angle-closure

c. Congenital

d. Secondary

9. If a patient is admitted for glaucoma, and the stage of the glaucoma evolves during admission, what should the coder do?

a. Assign the code for the highest stage of glaucoma documented.

b. Assign the code for the stage of glaucoma documented at admission.

c. Assign the code for the state of glaucoma documented at discharge.

d. Assign the one code for each stage of glaucoma documented.

10. Which of the following modifiers would be used to identify a procedure performed on the lower left eyelid?

a. E1

b. E2

c. E3

d. E4

Labeling

Instructions: Complete the following anatomical diagrams with the correct labels to identify the anatomy of the eye, eye muscles, and lacrimal apparatus.

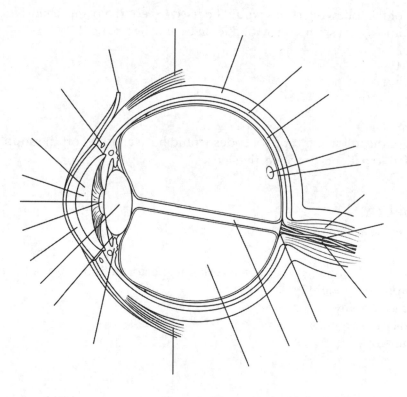

Source: ©AHIMA, figure 9.2, p. 275.

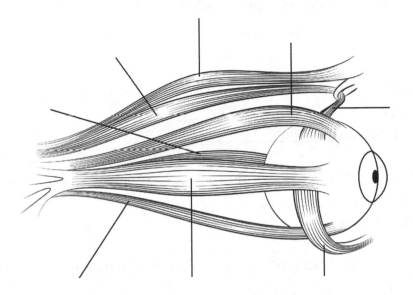

Source: ©AHIMA, figure 9.2, p. 276.

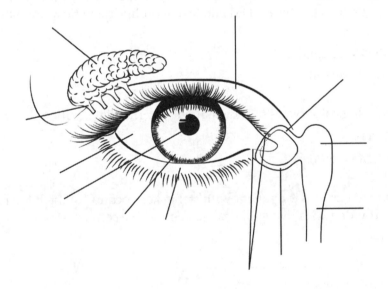

Source: ©AHIMA, figure 9.2, p. 275.

Coding

Instructions: Assign the correct CPT and ICD-10-CM codes for the following.

1. Code for the evisceration of ocular contents without subsequent implant due to chronic vitreous abscess of the right eye

CPT code(s): _____-_____

ICD-10-CM code(s): _____

2. Anterior removal of retained metallic foreign body of the posterior wall of the globe of the left eye via magnetic extraction

CPT code(s): _____-_____

ICD-10-CM code(s): _____, _____

3. Bilateral correction of both lower eyelids via electrosurgery epilation

CPT code(s): _____-_____, _____-_____

ICD-10-CM code(s): _____, _____

4. Single-stage ICCE procedure of the bilateral eyes for senile nuclear cataracts

CPT code(s): _____-_____

ICD-10-CM code(s): _____

5. Repair of retinal detachment with single break of the right eye via photocoagulation

CPT code(s): _____-_____

ICD-10-CM code(s): _____

6. Bilateral fluorescein angiography with interpretation and report, performed on 56-year-old male with type 2 DM and stable prolific diabetic retinopathy of the bilateral eyes

CPT code(s): _____

ICD-10-CM code(s): _____

7. Ophthalmological services for new patient, intermediate; patient has presbyopia

CPT code(s): _____

ICD-10-CM code(s): _____

8. Fitting of contact lens for patient with stable keratoconus of the bilateral eyes; patient provided with two spherical gas permeable contact lenses

CPT code(s): _____

HCPCS code(s): _____ × _____

ICD-10-CM code(s): _____

9. Patient supplied with one pair of spectacle frames fitted with two lenses: trifocal sphere plano to 4.00d (right lens) and triphocal sphere plan to 6.50 (left lens) in patient with presbyopia

HCPCS code(s): _____, _____-_____, _____-_____

ICD-10-CM code(s): _____

10. Prescription of corneal lens for congenital aphakia of the right eye, with fitting provided by independent technician

CPT code(s): _____-_____

ICD-10-CM code(s): _____

CHAPTER

Urgent Care and Emergency Department Services

Vocabulary

Instructions: Define each of the following key terms in the space provided.

1. Appendicitis: _____

_____

_____

2. Burn codes: _____

_____

_____

3. Cardiopulmonary resuscitation (CPR): _____

_____

_____

4. Closed procedure: _____

_____

_____

5. Corrosion codes: _____

_____

_____

6. Dislocation reduction: _____

_____

_____

7. Emergency services: _____

_____

_____

8. Emergent: _____

_____

_____

9. Endotracheal intubation: _____

_____

_____

10. Foreign body (FB): _____

_____

_____

11. Hemothorax: _____

_____

_____

12. Incision and drainage (I&D): _____

_____

_____

13. Lumbar puncture: _____

_____

_____

14. Lund-Browder classification: _____

_____

_____

15. Moderate (conscious) sedation: _____

_____

_____

16. Motor vehicle accident (MVA): _____

_____

_____

17. Myocardial infarction: _____

_____

_____

18. Nasal packing: _____

_____

_____

19. Open procedure: _____

_____

_____

20. Oximetry: _____

_____

_____

21. Penetrating wound: _____

_____

_____

22. Pleural effusion: _____

_____

_____

23. Pneumothorax: _____

_____

_____

24. Professional component: _____

_____

_____

25. Rule of nines: _____

_____

_____

26. Sepsis: _____

_____

_____

27. Septic shock: _____

_____

_____

28. Systemic inflammatory response syndrome (SIRS): _____

_____

_____

29. Technical component: _____

_____

_____

30. Thoracostomy: _____

_____

_____

31. Tracheostomy: _____

_____

_____

32. Tracheotomy: _____

_____

_____

33. Urgent care: _____

_____

_____

Multiple Choice

Instructions: Choose the best answer.

1. If an emergency service is not indicated as "Y" for emergency in box 24.C of the CMS-1500 claim form, which of the following things might happen?
   a. The service will require a prior authorization before it can be performed.
   b. The patient will have to wait until the next business day to receive the procedure.
   c. The insurance company may not pay for the service.
   d. The insurance will pay for the service, this box is for informational purposes only.

2. If an urgent care center does not have the resources to treat a patient's medical condition, what might the urgent care center do?
   a. Call an ambulance to transport the patient to the emergency department.
   b. Call the patient's family to come and take the patient home.
   c. Call the patient's primary care provider to make an appointment.
   d. Provide as much care as possible and then discharge the patient.

3. Which of the following types of urgent care procedures involves the use of diagnostic procedures to test patient specimens?
   a. X-rays and imaging procedures
   b. Laboratory tests
   c. Wound repair
   d. Oximetry

4. Which of the following ECG procedures describes only the technical component of the procedure?
   a. 93000
   b. 93005
   c. 93010
   d. No ECG codes describe only the technical components of the procedure

5. Which of the following types of wound repair includes layered closure of one or more deeper layers of subcutaneous tissue?
   a. Simple
   b. Complex
   c. Complete
   d. Intermediate

6. Which of the following are the three components of wound repair procedure codes?
   a. Site, depth, and extent
   b. Complexity, site, and length
   c. Length, site, and area
   d. Depth, width, and complexity

7. Which of the following procedure codes identifies an emergency procedure in which a tube is inserted through the mouth and into the trachea?
   a. 31500
   b. 31603
   c. 31605
   d. 31600

8. Which of the following external causes of injury codes identifies what the patient was doing when the injury occurred?
   a. External cause status
   b. Injury mechanism
   c. Place of occurrence
   d. Patient activity

9. Sepsis is considered severe sepsis when it presents with which of the following?
   a. Acute organ failure
   b. Septicemia
   c. Systemic inflammatory response syndrome (SIRS)
   d. Septic shock

10. Which of the following divides the body's surface into differing percentage based on the age of the patient?
    a. Rule of nines
    b. Extent of the burn
    c. Lund-Browder classification
    d. Corrosive classification system

Completion

Instructions: Complete the following flowchart with the decision process for when to code signs and symptoms versus a definitive diagnosis.

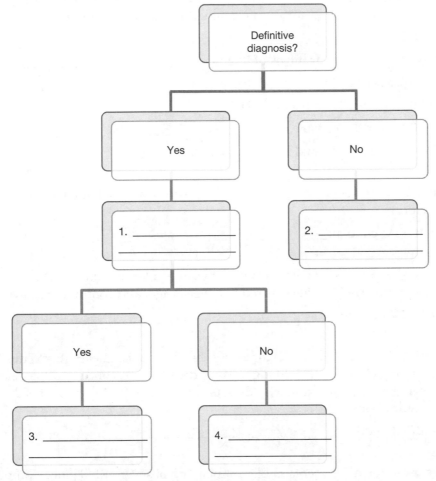

Source: Adapted from figure 10.11, p. 321.

Coding

Instructions: Assign the correct CPT and ICD-10-CM codes for the following.

1. 43-year-old patient presents to the emergency department with sepsis of unknown infectious origin, experiencing acute respiratory failure without septic shock. Provider completes a detailed history, comprehensive examination, and high complexity MDM.

   CPT code(s): _____

   ICD-10-CM code(s): _____, _____, _____

2. 14-year-old male patient presents to the ED after having suffered burns to both hands, arms, and chest. Burns are as follows: second degree burns of bilateral hands, 6 percent TBSA; second degree burns of the bilateral forearms, 6 percent TBSA; second degree burn of upper chest, 10 percent TBSA; Also has a small area of third-degree burn on the left cheek, approx. 1 percent TBSA. ED provider performed a detailed history and examination with moderate complexity MDM.

CPT code(s): _____

ICD-10-CM code(s) for burns of hands: _____, _____

ICD-10-CM code(s) for burns of forearms: _____, _____

ICD-10-CM code for burn of chest: _____

ICD-10-CM code for burn of face: _____

ICD-10-CM code for total body surface area: _____

3. Patient XYZ presents with acute non-ST anterior wall MI. Patient also has atrial fibrillation.

ICD-10-CM code(s): _____

4. Patient XYZ returns two weeks later with acute anterior wall STEMI. Still under care for her initial MI that occurred two weeks ago, and continues to have A Fib.

ICD-10-CM code(s): _____

5. Patient XYZ returns to the ED three months after her last heart attack, this time complaining of an overwhelming sense of dread. She is concerned that she is experiencing another heart attack. All tests are negative for MI; patient is diagnosed with panic attack.

ICD-10-CM code(s): _____, _____

6. 18-year-old female presents to ED complaining of severe RLQ pain. Computed tomography of abdomen without contrast reveals enlarged appendix. Clinical impression: acute appendicitis. Expanded problem-focused history and examination, MDM of low complexity.

CPT code(s): _____, _____

ICD-10-CM code(s): _____

7. Patient presents with multiple open wounds, which were closed as follows: intermediate repair of 4 cm laceration of right chest wall (no penetration into thoracic cavity); complex 2 cm repair of puncture wound of right abdomen (left upper quadrant, no puncture of peritoneal cavity); intermediate repair of two 3 cm lacerations of the left forearm, and simple repair of 1 cm laceration of the left hand. (Tip: When sequencing, remember to sequence the most complex repairs first, and to use a modifier to identify that additional repairs were distinct procedural services.)

CPT code(s): _____, _____-_____,

_____-_____

ICD-10-CM code(s): _____, _____, _____,

_____

8. 18-year-old male patient presents to the urgent care clinic in the evening hours on a weekday complaining of trouble breathing after a soccer match. He has a history of exercise-induced asthma, which is mostly controllable with a rescue inhaler, but he is currently experiencing shortness of breath, wheezing, and faintness. Pulse oximetry performed in the office reveals oxygen level of 89, and patient states that he has used his rescue inhaler three times in the last two hours with no relief. Inhaled pressurized nebulizer treatment administered in clinic. Physician documented a comprehensive history, comprehensive examination, and high complexity MDM for this new patient encounter. Clinical impression: exercise-induced bronchospasm. (Tip: Use additional codes to identify that the service was performed during regularly scheduled evening hours as well as the HCPCS code to identify that the service was performed in an urgent care center,)

CPT code(s): _____-_____, _____, _____,

_____, _____

ICD-10-CM code(s): _____

9. 27-year-old established female presents to the urgent care clinic during normal working hours complaining of nausea, vomiting, and lethargy. After a detailed history, expanded problem-focused examination, and MDM of low complexity, the provider diagnoses the patient with acute gastroenteritis. Patient also elects to get the flu mist nasal vaccine (LAIV3) while in the office, which is administered at the time of the encounter.

CPT code(s): _____-_____,

_____, _____, _____

ICD-10-CM code(s): _____

10. Transtracheal tracheostomy performed emergently in the ED for patient with laryngeal fracture.

CPT code(s): _____

ICD-10-CM code(s): _____

CHAPTER

11

Surgical Services

MOD

Vocabulary

Instructions: Define each of the following key terms in the space provided.

1. Ablation: _____

_____

_____

2. Admitting provider: _____

_____

_____

3. Allograft: _____

_____

_____

4. Ambulatory surgical center (ASC): _____

_____

_____

5. Appendectomy: _____

_____

_____

6. Appendicitis: _____

_____

_____

7. Autograft: _____

_____

_____

8. Block: _____

_____

_____

9. Cadaver donor: _____

_____

_____

10. Cholangiography: _____

_____

_____

11. Cholangitis: _____

_____

_____

12. Cholecystectomy: _____

_____

_____

13. Cholecystitis: _____

_____

_____

14. Choledocholithiasis: _____

_____

_____

15. Cholelithiasis: _____

_____

_____

16. Code edit: _____

_____

_____

17. Comorbid condition: _____

_____

_____

18. Complication of care: _____

_____

_____

19. Debridement: _____

_____

_____

20. Destruction: _____

_____

_____

21. Diagnostic procedure: _____

_____

_____

22. Diaphragm: _____

_____

_____

23. Endoscopy: _____

_____

_____

24. Excised diameter: _____

_____

_____

25. Excision: _____

_____

_____

26. Global period: _____

_____

_____

27. Global surgical package: _____

_____

_____

28. Homograft: _____

_____

_____

29. Incidental appendectomy: _____

_____

_____

30. Incision: _____

_____

_____

31. Introduction: _____

_____

_____

32. Laparoscopy: _____

_____

_____

33. Living donor: _____

_____

_____

34. Manipulation: _____

_____

_____

35. Margin: _____

_____

_____

36. Mediastinum: _____

_____

_____

37. Mohs micrographic surgery: _____

_____

_____

38. National Correct Coding Initiative (NCCI): _____

_____

_____

39. Never events: _____

_____

_____

40. Non-pressure ulcer: _____

_____

_____

41. Outpatient: _____

_____

_____

42. Outpatient hospital: _____

_____

_____

43. Paring: _____

_____

_____

44. Performing provider: _____

_____

_____

45. Peritonitis: _____

_____

_____

46. Postoperative diagnosis: _____

_____

_____

47. Preoperative diagnosis: _____

_____

_____

48. Pressure ulcer: _____

_____

_____

49. Removal: _____

_____

_____

50. Repair: _____

_____

_____

51. Resection: _____

_____

_____

52. Rhinoplasty: _____

_____

_____

53. Robot-assisted surgery: _____

_____

_____

54. Separate procedure: _____

_____

_____

55. Shaving: _____

_____

_____

56. Skin lesion: _____

_____

_____

57. Skin ulcer: _____

_____

_____

58. Stage: _____

_____

_____

59. Surgical procedure: _____

_____

_____

60. Therapeutic procedure: _____

_____

_____

61. Transplantation: _____

_____

_____

62. Unbundling: _____

_____

_____

63. Xenograft: _____

_____

_____

Word Bank

Instructions: Using the proedures listed, complete the following table to describe the components of surgical packages.

Wound repair

Diagnostic endoscopy

Pacemaker insertion

Major surgical procedure

Simple procedure

Minor surgical procedure

Zero Day Global Period	10-Day Global Period	90-Day Global Period

Matching

Instructions: Match the Surgery subsection with the code range for that section.

1. _____ Integumentary   **A.** 54000 to 55899

2. _____ Musculoskeletal   **B.** 69000 to 69979

3. _____ Respiratory   **C.** 30000 to 32999

4. _____ Cardiovascular   **D.** 60000 to 60699

5. _____ Hemic and Lymphatic   **E.** 39000 to 39599

6. _____ Mediastinum and Diaphragm   **F.** 10030 to 19499

7. _____ Digestive   **G.** 56405 to 58999

8. _____ Urinary   **H.** 33010 to 37799

9. _____ Male Genital   **I.** 20005 to 29999

10. _____ Female Genital   **J.** 40490 to 49999

11. _____ Maternity Care and Delivery   **K.** 38100 to 38999

12. _____ Endocrine System   **L.** 59000 to 59899

13. _____ Nervous System   **M.** 61000 to 64999

14. _____ Eye and Ocular Adnexa   **N.** 65091 to 68899

15. _____ Auditory System   **O.** 50010 to 53899

Completion

Instructions: There are three components to endoscopy coding. Name and describe each of the three components and give one example of how each of these components may impact code selection.

1. _____

_____

2. _____

_____

3. _____

_____

Coding

Instructions: Identify only the modifier for the following procedural descriptions.

1. Anesthesia provided by the surgeon for a child undergoing a foreign body removal procedure

   Modifier: _____

2. Procedure performed on the bilateral arms

   Modifier: _____

3. Surgical team of four physicians completed a complex surgery of the skull base

   Modifier: _____

4. Patient undergoing an endoscopic examination of the bronchus began experiencing respiratory difficulties, so the endoscope was removed and the procedure was discontinued

   Modifier: _____

5. Ophthalmological surgeon performed the intraoperative services only for a procedure involving the removal and insertion of a cataract prosthesis

   Modifier: _____

6. Open heart procedure performed on a two-month-old infant weighing 7 lbs (3.5 kg)

   Modifier: _____

7. A normally bilateral procedure (CPT code for procedure identifies a bilateral service) is completed unilaterally

   Modifier: _____

8. Anterior cervical discectomy with arthrodesis required additional work to dissect through unusually thick tissue and ligaments (extra work was substantially greater than what is typically required for the service)

   Modifier: _____

9. Patient with Alzheimer's dementia with behavioral disturbances suffered chest lacerations after falling in his kitchen; due to extreme aggression, the patient was placed under general anesthesia in order to repair the chest wounds

   Modifier: _____

10. 10 days after pacemaker insertion, the patient was returned to the operating room (in the global period) because the patient was experiencing electrical shocks from the device; the entire pacemaker and all leads were removed and replaced with new functioning parts

Modifier: _____

11. Plastic surgeon assisted in wound repair surgery for patient with multiple open wounds

Modifier: _____

12. Team of surgeons consisting of one cardiologist and one pulmonologist performed a thoracic repair procedure

Modifier: _____

13. General surgeon minimally assisted in transplantation surgery

Modifier: _____

14. Colorectal surgeon completed only the postoperative and follow-up care for a patient who underwent a colectomy

Modifier: _____

15. Orthopedic specialist performed only the preoperative evaluation and consultation services to a patient undergoing a bilateral total knee arthroplasty

Modifier: _____

Instructions: Identify only the procedure and diagnosis code for the following.

16. Excision of tumor of carotid body with sparing of carotid artery

CPT code(s): _____

ICD-10-CM code(s): _____

17. Surgical treatment of papillary thyroid carcinoma with total unilateral thyroid lobectomy of the left thyroid, with contralateral subtotal lobectomy of the right lobe, including isthmusectomy; functional activity of the neoplasm includes corticoadrenal insufficiency and hypopituitarism

CPT code(s): _____

ICD-10-CM code(s): _____, _____, _____

18. Excision of stage 4 coccygeal pressure ulcer with removal of portion of coccyx bone and flap closure

CPT code(s): _____

ICD-10-CM code(s): _____

19. Biopsy of uvula (palate) for neoplasm of uncertain behavior of the uvula

CPT code(s): _____

ICD-10-CM code(s): _____

20. Open drainage of renal abscess

CPT code(s): _____

ICD-10-CM code(s): _____

21. Laparoscopic unilateral orchiectomy of the right descended testicle for testicular cancer

CPT code(s): _____

ICD-10-CM code(s): _____

22. Destruction (chemodenervation) of axillary eccrine sweat glands for primary focal hyperhidrosis of the axilla

CPT code(s): _____

ICD-10-CM code(s): _____

23. Unlisted procedure of the accessory sinuses

CPT code(s): _____

24. Bronchoscopy with revision of previously placed bronchial stent and bronchial dilation for congenital stenosis of bilateral bronchus

CPT code(s): _____

ICD-10-CM code(s): _____

25. Bronchoscopy with bronchial alveolar lavage and endobronchial biopsy for patient with alveolar pneumopathy

CPT code(s): _____, _____-_____

ICD-10-CM code(s): _____

26. Robotic-assisted cholecystectomy in patient with calculus of gallbladder with chronic cholecystitis with obstruction. (Tip: Check for a HCPCS code to indicate that the surgery was performed with robotic assistance.)

CPT code(s): _____, _____

ICD-10-CM code(s): _____

CHAPTER

Anesthesia and Pain Management Services

Vocabulary

Instructions: Define each of the following key terms in the space provided.

1. Acupuncture: _____

_____

_____

2. Analgesia: _____

_____

_____

3. Anesthesia services: _____

_____

_____

4. Anesthesiology: _____

_____

_____

5. ASA crosswalk: _____

_____

_____

6. Base units: _____

_____

_____

7. Cervicalgia: _____

_____

_____

8. Chronic pain: _____

_____

_____

9. Conversion factor (CF): _____

_____

_____

10. Electrodiagnostic studies: _____

_____

_____

11. Electromyography (EMG): _____

_____

_____

12. Enthesopathy: _____

_____

_____

13. Epidural steroid injection: _____

_____

_____

14. Facet joint injection: _____

_____

_____

15. Fibromyalgia: _____

_____

_____

16. General anesthesia: _____

_____

_____

17. Integrative medicine: _____

_____

_____

18. Interventional pain procedures: _____

_____

_____

19. Kyphoplasty: _____

_____

_____

20. Local anesthesia: _____

_____

_____

21. Lumbago: _____

_____

_____

22. Moderate (conscious) sedation: _____

_____

_____

23. Modifying factors: _____

_____

_____

24. Monitored anesthesia care (MAC): _____

_____

_____

25. Myalgia: _____

_____

_____

26. Myositis: _____

_____

_____

27. Nerve condition study (NCS): _____

_____

_____

28. Occipital nerve block: _____

_____

_____

29. Osteoarthritis: _____

_____

_____

30. Pain management services: _____

_____

_____

31. Peripheral nerve stimulation: _____

_____

_____

32. Physical status modifier: _____

_____

_____

33. Qualifying circumstance CPT codes: _____

_____

_____

34. Radiculopathy: _____

_____

_____

35. Radiofrequency nerve ablation: _____

_____

_____

36. Regional anesthesia: _____

_____

_____

37. Sciatica: _____

_____

_____

38. Spinal cord stimulation (SCS): _____

_____

_____

39. Time units: _____

_____

_____

Multiple Choice

Instructions: Choose the best answer.

1. Which of the following medical providers is a medical doctor who provides analgesia to patients?
   a. Anesthesiology assistant
   b. Certified registered nurse anesthetist
   c. Anesthesiologist
   d. Physician assistant

2. Which of the following produces an incomplete loss of consciousness, which allows the patient to be sedated but awake at the same time?
   a. Moderate sedation
   b. Regional anesthesia
   c. General anesthesia
   d. Local anesthesia

3. Which of the following employs an injection to block a large amount of nerves?
   a. Moderate sedation
   b. Regional anesthesia
   c. General anesthesia
   d. Local anesthesia

4. Which of the following anesthesia modifiers would be used for an anesthesia service provided by a CRNA under the medical direction of a physician?
   a. QX
   b. QZ
   c. AA
   d. QY

5. Which of the following procedures uses a controlled heat source to disable nerves as a treatment for back or neck pain?
   a. Joint injections
   b. Moderate sedation
   c. Nerve blocks
   d. Radiofrequency nerve ablation

6. Which of the following procedure codes would be reported if the patient has a past history of failed moderate sedation?
   a. T88.4
   b. T88.51
   c. Z92.83
   d. Z92.84

7. Which of the following codes would be reported if a patient presented with chronic pain caused by a malignancy in the lung?
   a. G89.1
   b. G89.18
   c. G89.29
   d. G89.3

Fill in the Blank

Instructions: Complete the following for anesthesia services.

1. _____ units describe the relative values for anesthesia services.

2. _____ units identify how much time was spent on an anesthesia service, from start to finish.

3. _____ _____ identify special circumstances of the anesthesia procedure or the health of the patient.

4. The _____ _____ modifier identifies the health of the patient.

5. _____ _____ codes identify special circumstances surrounding the anesthesia service.

6. The _____ _____ is the dollar amount used to calculate the charge amount for an anesthesia service.

7. Charges for anesthesia services are determined based on the following calculation:

(_____ + _____ + _____)

✗

_____ = total charge amount

Matching

Instructions: Match the Surgery subsection with the code range for that section.

1. _____ 99100   **A.** Anesthesia complicated by utilization of total body hypothermia

2. _____ 99116   **B.** Anesthesia complicated by utilization of controlled hypotension

3. _____ 99135   **C.** Anesthesia for patient of extreme age

4. _____ 99140   **D.** Anesthesia complicated by emergency conditions

Labeling

Instructions: Complete the following anatomical diagram with the correct labels to identify the levels of the spine.

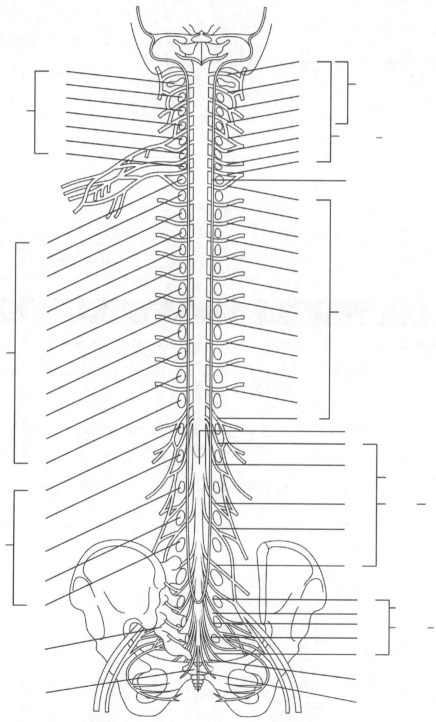

Source: ©AHIMA, figure 12.12, p. 420.

Coding

Instructions: Identify the correct CPT and ICD-10-CM codes for the following statements.

1. Anesthesia for pulmonary resection and thoracoplasty in a normal healthy patient

   CPT code(s): _____-_____

2. Anesthesia for physiological support for harvesting of organs from brain-dead patient

   CPT code(s): _____-_____

3. Anesthesia for repair of cleft palate in normal healthy patient, aged 3 years, with cleft hard palate

   CPT code(s): _____-_____

   ICD-10-CM code(s): _____

4. Anesthesia performed for pneumocentesis for moribund patient with traumatic hemothorax; patient presented under emergency conditions after MVA

   CPT code(s): _____-_____, _____

   ICD-10-CM code(s): _____

5. 30 minutes of acupuncture with electrical stimulation performed on 42-year-old female patient with lumbago with sciatica of the right and left sides

   CPT code(s): _____, _____

   ICD-10-CM code(s): _____, _____

6. Fluoroscopy-guided bilateral facet joint injections of the lumbar spine at L2 and L3 for patient with lumbago

   CPT code(s): _____-_____, _____-_____

   ICD-10-CM code(s): _____

7. Anesthesia for normal healthy patient with bilateral vasectomy for elective sterilization

   CPT code(s): _____-_____

   ICD-10-CM code(s): _____

8. Placement of indwelling catheter for continuous administration of anesthetic substance into the interlaminar epidural into the lumbar area, with imaging guidance, for patient with chronic low back pain and left-sided sciatica

   CPT code(s): _____

   ICD-10-CM code(s): _____, _____

9. Chemodenervation by neurolytic destruction of L4-L5, L5-L6, and L6-L7 facets joints bilaterally for patient with lumbar radiculopathy

    CPT code(s): _____, _____-_____ (×_____)

    ICD-10-CM code(s): _____

10. Kyphoplasty of T2 and T3 vertebrae for treatment of collapsed vertebra

    CPT code(s): _____, _____

    ICD-10-CM code(s): _____

CHAPTER

Radiology and Imaging Services

Vocabulary

Instructions: Define each of the following key terms in the space provided.

1. Anterior: _____

_____

_____

2. Antero-posterior: _____

_____

_____

3. Axial plane: _____

_____

_____

4. Computed tomography (CT): _____

_____

_____

5. Contralateral: _____

_____

_____

6. Contrast material: _____

_____

_____

7. Coronal plane: _____

_____

_____

8. Distal: _____

_____

_____

9. Doppler ultrasound: _____

_____

_____

10. Global radiology service: _____

_____

_____

11. Imaging services: _____

_____

_____

12. Independent radiology and imaging center: _____

_____

_____

13. Inferior: _____

_____

_____

14. Ipsilateral: _____

_____

_____

15. Lateral: _____

_____

_____

16. Lateral (view): _____

_____

_____

17. Magnetic resonance imaging (MRI): _____

_____

_____

18. Mammography: _____

_____

_____

19. Medial: _____

_____

_____

20. Nuclear medicine: _____

_____

_____

21. Oblique: _____

_____

_____

22. Pleural effusion: _____

_____

_____

23. Posterior: _____

_____

_____

24. Postero-anterior: _____

_____

_____

25. Professional component (PC): _____

_____

_____

26. Projection: _____

_____

_____

27. Proximal: _____

_____

_____

28. Pulmonary edema: _____

_____

_____

29. Radiologic guidance: _____

_____

_____

30. Radiological supervision and interpretation (S&I): _____

_____

_____

31. Radiologist: _____

_____

_____

32. Radiology services: _____

_____

_____

33. Sagittal plane: _____

_____

_____

34. Superior: _____

_____

_____

35. Technical component (TC): _____

_____

_____

36. Transverse plane: _____

_____

_____

37. Ultrasound: _____

_____

_____

38. X-ray: _____

_____

_____

Multiple Choice

Instructions: Choose the best answer.

1. Which of the following projection passes through the back to the front of the body?
   a. Oblique
   b. Lateral
   c. Poster-anterior
   d. Antero-posterior

2. Which of the following modifiers identifies the professional component of a service?
   a. -26
   b. -TC
   c. -25
   d. -RT

3. Which of the following modifiers identifies the technical component of a service?
   a. -26
   b. -RT
   c. -LT
   d. -TC

4. Radiological supervision and interpretation (S&I) is another term used for which of the following?
   a. Technical component
   b. Performing the imaging service
   c. Professional component
   d. Ordering the imaging service

5. Which of the following modifiers is reported to identify a global imaging service?
   a. -26
   b. -TC
   c. Both -26 and -TC
   d. No modifier would be used

6. Which of the following types of radiology procedures uses strong magnetic fields and radio waves to produce images of the internal structures of the body?
   a. MRI
   b. X-ray
   c. CT
   d. PET

7. Which of the following diagnostic studies uses soundwaves to view a specific area of the body?
   a. PET
   b. Ultrasound
   c. X-ray
   d. Nuclear imaging

8. Which of the following mammograms is performed on a regular basis to detect early changes in the breast, which may indicate breast cancer?
   a. Diagnostic
   b. Therapeutic
   c. Screening
   d. Presumptive

9. Which of the following mammograms is performed when a patient has a clinical sign or symptom of the breast?
   a. Diagnostic
   b. Therapeutic
   c. Screening
   d. Presumptive

10. If a patient presents to the office for treatment and the provider performs an x-ray to diagnose the patient, and then the same provider performs an additional x-ray after a therapeutic service, which of the following modifiers would be used?
a. -50
b. No modifier would be used for the global service
c. -77
d. -76

Matching

Instructions: Match the Surgery subsection with the code range for that section.

1. _____ Anterior   **A.** Toward the midline of the body (the belly button)

2. _____ Posterior   **B.** Situated toward the back of the body (such as the buttocks or heels)

3. _____ Superior   **C.** Away from the body (the fingertips)

4. _____ Inferior   **D.** The opposite side of the body (the right arm and the left arm)

5. _____ Medial   **E.** Situated toward the front of the body (such as the face or the breasts)

6. _____ Lateral   **F.** The same side of the body (the right upper and lower extremities)

7. _____ Proximal   **G.** Away from the midline of the body (the sides)

8. _____ Distal   **H.** Toward the top of the body (the head)

9. _____ Ipsilateral   **I.** Toward the center of the body (the upper arm)

10. _____ Contralateral   **J.** Toward the bottom of the body (the feet)

Coding

Instructions: Identify the correct CPT and ICD-10-CM codes for the following statements.

1. MRI of the kidneys and liver with contrast (4ml octafluoropropane microspheres) in a patient with kidney failure. 2 cm mass of the liver identified.

CPT code(s): _____

HCPCS code(s): _____ × _____

ICD-10-CM code(s): _____

2. X-ray of the alimentary tract (nose to rectum) in 8-year-old child who accidentally swallowed three 0.5 cm magnets. Three foreign bodies identified: one in stomach and two in small intestine.

   CPT code(s): _____

   ICD-10-CM code(s): _____, _____

3. Transrectal ultrasound for patient with benign prostatic hyperplasia.

   CPT code(s): _____

   ICD-10-CM code(s): _____

4. Vertebral fracture assessment via dual-energy x-ray absorptiometry (DXA) in 80-year-old female patient with collapsed vertebra of the T4 and T5.

   CPT code(s): _____

   ICD-10-CM code(s): _____

5. Nuclear imaging study of the joints of the lower extremities, including hips, for patient with bilateral acute osteomyelitis of the lower legs.

   CPT code(s): _____

   ICD-10-CM code(s): _____, _____

6. X-ray of the left hip (three views) in 75-year-old patient who suffered a fall and is now complaining of unilateral hip pain. No fractures identified.

   CPT code(s): _____

   ICD-10-CM code(s): _____

7. Complete retroperitoneal ultrasound reveals staghorn calculus of the left kidney.

   CPT code(s): _____

   ICD-10-CM code(s): _____

8. Complete osseous survey in a 20-day-old female patient.

   CPT code(s): _____

9. Fetal biophysical profile without nonstress testing completed via ultrasound on female patient with pregnancy complicated by blood clotting disease in the second trimester.

   CPT code(s): _____

   ICD-10-CM code(s): _____

10. CT colonography with and without contrast for 36-year-old obese male with intestinal adhesions with incomplete obstruction.

    CPT code(s): _____

    ICD-10-CM code(s): _____, _____

CHAPTER 14

Laboratory and Pathology Services

Vocabulary

Instructions: Define each of the following key terms in the space provided.

1. Bacteriology: _____

_____

_____

2. Cytopathology: _____

_____

_____

3. Frozen block: _____

_____

_____

4. Frozen section: _____

_____

_____

5. Gross examination: _____

_____

_____

6. Independent laboratory: _____

_____

_____

7. Laboratory and pathology services: _____

_____

_____

8. Methicillin-resistant *Staphylococcus aureus* (MRSA): _____

_____

_____

9. Methicillin-susceptible *Staphylococcus aureus* (MSSA): _____

_____

_____

10. Microscopic examination: _____

_____

_____

11. Mycology: _____

_____

_____

12. Nonspecific test: _____

_____

_____

13. Panel: _____

_____

_____

14. Parasitology: _____

_____

_____

15. Pass-through billing: _____

_____

_____

16. Permanent block: _____

_____

_____

17. Permanent section: _____

_____

_____

18. Qualitative examination: _____

_____

_____

19. Quantitative examination: _____

_____

_____

20. Smear: _____

_____

_____

21. Specific test: _____

_____

_____

22. Specimen: _____

_____

_____

23. Virology: _____

_____

_____

Multiple Choice

Instructions: Choose the best answer.

1. In which of the following laboratories are the procedures typically low-risk, lox-complexity procedures?
   a. CLIA-waived laboratories
   b. Independent laboratories
   c. Hospital laboratories
   d. Practice-dependent laboratories

2. Which of the following would not be classified as a CLIA-waived laboratory test?
   a. Mono spot
   b. Strep swab
   c. Gene analysis
   d. Urinalysis

3. In pass-through billing, which modifier is appended to the CPT code for the laboratory service to indicate that it was performed by an independent laboratory?
   a. -81
   b. -90
   c. -59
   d. -91

4. In pass-through billing, the charges for the laboratory service are entered into which box on the CMS-1500 form?
   a. Box 24.A
   b. Box 90
   c. Box 21
   d. Box 20

5. Which of the following levels of surgical pathology procedures includes only the gross examination of a specimen?
   a. Level I
   b. Level II
   c. Level III
   d. Level IV

Fill in the Blank

Instructions: Complete the following statements.

1. In pass-through billing, the three things you must do on the CMS-1500 form are: change the place of service to _____; add the charges in box _____ of the CMS-1500 claim form; and append modifier _____ to the CPT code for the _____.

2. Laboratory services identify only the _____ of the specimen. CPT codes from the surgical section of the CPT code book are required to identify the _____ of the specimen.

3. After specimens are collected, they may be examined in a number of different ways. _____ is an examination of the physical characteristics of a specimen. _____ is the examination of a specimen at a microscopic level, which allows the pathologist to see the cells of the specimen. A _____ is a specimen that is submerged into liquid or a fluid substance, and then smeared onto the surface of a slide. A _____ is a small slice of a specimen that has been frozen; and a _____ is a small slice of a specimen that has been preserved in a fixative agent.

4. A _____ examination is one that examines the characteristics or properties of a specimen. A _____ examination is one that determines the amount of a substance within a specimen.

Coding

Instructions: Identify the correct CPT and ICD-10-CM codes for the following statements.

1. Collection of venous blood by venipuncture for complete blood count (automated with differential) in patient with upper respiratory infection

CPT code(s): _____, _____

ICD-10-CM code(s): _____

2. 45-year-old established male presents to the office for routine physical examination; complete lipid panel completed in office, which revealed hypercholesterolemia

CPT code(s): _____, _____

ICD-10-CM code(s): _____, _____

3. HIV confirmation test on patient with recently diagnosed asymptomatic HIV status

CPT code(s): _____

ICD-10-CM code(s): _____

4. Postmortem examination of stillborn infant (including brain)

CPT code(s): _____

5. Pathological examination of prostatic tissue obtained from transurethral resection of the prostate, performed for benign prostatic hypertrophy

CPT code(s): _____

ICD-10-CM code(s): _____

6. Electrolyte panel completed on a patient with dehydration and electrolyte imbalance

   CPT code(s): _____

   ICD-10-CM code(s): _____

7. Adenovirus antibody test performed on patient with upper respiratory infection and diarrhea

   CPT code(s): _____

   ICD-10-CM code(s): _____, _____

8. Serologic Rh (D) blood typing test performed on G1P0 patient at 8 weeks' gestation

   CPT code(s): _____

9. Vaginal chlamydial culture for patient who engages in high-risk heterosexual behavior, with vaginal discharge and pelvic pain confirming chlamydial vulvovaginitis

   CPT code(s): _____

   ICD-10-CM code(s): _____, _____

10. HIV-1 antigen and HIV-2 antibody tests performed on a fully transportable testing platform confirms asymptomatic HIV status

    CPT code(s): _____-_____

    ICD-10-CM code(s): _____

CHAPTER 15

Orthopedic Services

MOD

Vocabulary

Instructions: Define each of the following key terms in the space provided.

1. Amputation: _____

_____

_____

2. Arthritis: _____

_____

_____

3. Arthrocentesis: _____

_____

_____

4. Arthrodesis: _____

_____

_____

5. Arthropathy: _____

_____

_____

6. Arthroplasty: _____

_____

_____

7. Arthroscopy: _____

_____

_____

8. Closed fracture: _____

_____

_____

9. Closed treatment: _____

_____

_____

10. Comminuted fracture: _____

_____

_____

11. Compound fracture: _____

_____

_____

12. Compression fracture: _____

_____

_____

13. Displaced fracture: _____

_____

_____

14. Greenstick fracture: _____

_____

_____

15. Gustilo-Anderson classification: _____

_____

_____

16. Impacted fracture: _____

_____

_____

17. Internal fixation device: _____

_____

_____

18. Interspace: _____

_____

_____

19. Kyphosis: _____

_____

_____

20. Malunion: _____

_____

_____

21. Manipulation: _____

_____

_____

22. Monoarthritis: _____

_____

_____

23. Musculoskeletal system: _____

_____

_____

24. Non-displaced fracture: _____

_____

_____

25. Nonunion: _____

_____

_____

26. Oblique fracture: _____

_____

_____

27. Open fracture: _____

_____

_____

28. Open treatment: _____

_____

_____

29. Orthopedic services: _____

_____

_____

30. Orthopedist: _____

_____

_____

31. Osteoarthritis: _____

_____

_____

32. Pathological fracture: _____

_____

_____

33. Percutaneous: _____

_____

_____

34. Percutaneous skeletal fixation: _____

_____

_____

35. Physeal fracture: _____

_____

_____

36. Polyarthritis: _____

_____

_____

37. Salter-Harris classification: _____

_____

_____

38. Scoliosis: _____

_____

_____

39. Segment: _____

_____

_____

40. Segmental fracture: _____

_____

_____

41. Skeletal traction: _____

_____

_____

42. Skin traction: _____

_____

_____

43. Spiral fracture: _____

_____

_____

44. Sprain: _____

_____

_____

45. Strain: _____

_____

_____

46. Torus fracture: _____

_____

_____

47. Traction: _____

_____

_____

48. Transverse fracture: _____

_____

_____

49. Traumatic fracture: _____

_____

_____

Multiple Choice

Instructions: Choose the best answer.

1. Excisions of subcutaneous soft tissue tumors are for the removal of tissue:
a. Below the skin
b. Below the deep fascia
c. More than one layer of tissue
d. Of the bone

2. Which of the following types of procedures identifies the aspiration of a joint?
a. Arthrodesis
b. Arthrocentesis
c. Arthritis
d. Amputation

3. Which of the following types of traction uses straps, ropes, pulleys, and weights on the outside of the body?
a. Skeletal
b. Percutaneous
c. Internal
d. Skin

4. Which of the following types of fracture treatments involves the manual application of external forces to place the bone back to its original position?
a. Manipulation
b. Traction
c. Fixation
d. Rotation

5. Which of the following treatment types includes the incision of the skin in order to view the fracture site and/or place internal fixation devices?
a. Closed treatment
b. Percutaneous skeletal fixation
c. Open treatment
d. Internal fixation

6. In which of the following circumstances would it be appropriate to report the code for the casting of a fracture?
a. After the fracture is manipulated into place and then set
b. After the application of internal fixation devices
c. If no fracture manipulation or repair was performed
d. When the casting is an especially difficult procedure

7. Which of the following procedures involves the replacement of the knee joint?
a. Knee arthroplasty
b. Knee arthrodesis
c. Knee arthrocentesis
d. Knee amputation

8. Which of the following amputation codes would be reported to identify a midtarsal amputation?
   a. 28800
   b. 28805
   c. 28810
   d. 28820

9. Which of the following is used to identify the severity of a compound fracture?
   a. Salter-Harris classification
   b. Lund-Browder classification
   c. Gustilo-Anderson classification
   d. The rule of nines

10. Which of the following is used to identify the type of fracture that occurs on a growth plate?
    a. Salter-Harris classification
    b. Lund-Browder classification
    c. Gustilo-Anderson classification
    d. The rule of nines

Matching

Instructions: Match the fracture type with the fracture description.

1. _____ Greenstick

2. _____ Transverse

3. _____ Spiral

4. _____ Oblique

5. _____ Comminuted

6. _____ Segmental

7. _____ Torus

8. _____ Impacted

9. _____ Compression

A. Fracture found in the spine when vertebrae collapse under their own pressure

B. Fracture composed of at least two fracture lines that isolate a larger section of bone

C. Fracture spirals around and extends down the bone

D. Fracture travels horizontally across the bone

E. Ends of the bone are pushed into each other

F. Bone bends and cracks on one side

G. Fracture travels diagonally across the bone

H. Fracture in which only one part of the bone buckles, occurs in children

I. Fracture has more than two parts with multiple broken pieces

Coding

Instructions: Identify the correct CPT and ICD-10-CM codes for the following statements.

1. Report the code for a Salter-Harris type I physeal fracture of lower end of right femur, initial encounter for closed fracture.

ICD-10-CM code(s): _____

2. Percutaneous skeletal fixation of metatarsal bone for displaced fracture of fifth metatarsal bone of the left foot. (Tip: remember to identify the laterality of the procedure with the correct modifier.)

CPT code(s): _____-_____

ICD-10-CM code(s): _____

3. Patient with osteoporosis is seen for pain in right forearm after falling in her kitchen. 78-year-old female has age-related osteoporosis. X-ray of the forearm (two views) reveals nondisplaced fracture of the right radius. Static splint applied in office without manipulation for immobilization of fracture site and patient advised to return in one month for follow-up to check healing status.

CPT code(s): _____-_____, _____-_____

ICD-10-CM code(s): _____

4. Release of thenar muscle of the left hand due to thumb contracture.

CPT code(s): _____-_____

ICD-10-CM code(s): _____

5. Metatarsal amputation of great toe of right foot due to gangrene.

CPT code(s): _____-_____

ICD-10-CM code(s): _____

6. 80-year-old female presents for evaluation of her senile osteoporosis. She has no current osteoporotic fractures but does have a history of healed pathological fracture of her left radius and ulna.

ICD-10-CM code(s): _____, _____

7. Antibiotic injection without ultrasound guidance provided to 38-year-old male patient with MSSA infectious arthritis of right knee joint.

CPT code(s): _____-_____

ICD-10-CM code(s): _____, _____

8. 34-year-old male presents for a follow-up on an open (Type IIIB) displaced oblique fracture of the shaft of the right femur, which was surgically fixed and is now healing well. Cast was removed and replaced with an ambulatory long leg cast.

   CPT code(s): _____-_____

   ICD-10-CM code(s): _____

9. Incision and drainage of deep abscess of the lumbosacral spine.

   CPT code(s): _____

   ICD-10-CM code(s): _____

10. Arthrotomy of left glenohumeral joint for removal of foreign body of left shoulder remaining after a puncture wound.

    CPT code(s): _____-_____

    ICD-10-CM code(s): _____

CHAPTER

Physical, Occupational, and Speech Therapy Services

Vocabulary

Instructions: Define each of the following key terms in the space provided.

1. 8-minute rule: _____

_____

_____

2. Amputation: _____

_____

_____

3. Amputee: _____

_____

_____

4. Amyotrophic lateral sclerosis (ALS): _____

_____

_____

5. Aphonia: _____

_____

_____

6. Augmentative and alternative communication (AAC): _____

_____

_____

7. Cognitive communication disorder: _____

_____

_____

8. Constant attendance code: _____

_____

_____

9. Dentofacial anomaly: _____

_____

_____

10. Dominant side: _____

_____

_____

11. Dyslexia: _____

_____

_____

12. Dysphagia: _____

_____

_____

13. Electrical stimulation: _____

_____

_____

14. Hubbard tank: _____

_____

_____

15. Hypernasality: _____

_____

_____

16. Iontophoresis: _____

_____

_____

17. Language disorder: _____

_____

_____

18. Multiple sclerosis (MS): _____

_____

_____

19. Occupational therapist (OT): _____

_____

_____

20. Occupational therapy services: _____

_____

_____

21. Physical therapist (PT): _____

_____

_____

22. Physical therapy services: _____

_____

_____

23. Service-based code: _____

_____

_____

24. Social communication disorder: _____

_____

_____

25. Speech-language pathologist (SLP): _____

_____

_____

26. Speech therapy services: _____

_____

_____

27. Therapy services: _____

_____

_____

28. Time-based code: _____

_____

_____

29. Traumatic brain injury (TBI): _____

_____

_____

30. Treatment modality: _____

_____

_____

31. Vasopneumatic device: _____

_____

_____

Multiple Choice

Instructions: Choose the best answer.

1. Which of the following therapy types provides noninvasive treatments to alleviate pain and improve and restore functionality?
   a. Physical
   b. Occupational
   c. Speech

2. Which of the following therapy types helps adults and children improve their communication skills?
   a. Physical
   b. Occupational
   c. Speech

3. Which of the following therapy types helps patients improve fine motor skills?
   a. Physical
   b. Occupational
   c. Speech

4. Which of the following parties provides the advanced beneficiary notice?
   a. The provider performing the service
   b. The patient receiving the service
   c. The insurance expected to pay for the service
   d. The insurance expected to not pay for the service

5. Which of the following modifiers identifies that the ABN is on file at the provider's office?
   a. GX
   b. GA
   c. GY
   d. GZ

Matching

Instructions: Match the disorder or healthcare condition with its description.

1. _____ Language disorder

2. _____ Hypernasality

3. _____ Social communication disorder

4. _____ Aphonia

5. _____ Cognitive communication disorder

6. _____ Dyslexia

7. _____ Dysphagia

8. _____ Dysphasia

A. Excessive nasal tone to the voice

B. Difficulty organizing thoughts, remembering, paying attention, and planning

C. Difficulty in understanding or producing oral speech

D. Difficulty reading

E. Loss of voice

F. Difficulty understanding social cues and nonverbal communication

G. Difficulty swallowing

H. Difficulty speaking

Coding

Instructions: Identify the correct procedure and diagnosis codes for the following statements.

1. Low complexity physical therapy evaluation for a 53-year-old female with bilateral knee osteoarthritis

   CPT code(s): _____

   ICD-10-CM code(s): _____

2. Application of hot pack to right shoulder followed by 30 minutes of range of motion, strength, and flexibility therapy for patient with incomplete tear of rotator cuff of right shoulder

   CPT code(s): _____, _____ × _____

   ICD-10-CM code(s): _____

3. Repair of augmentative and alternative communication (AAC) device for patient with aphonia

   HCPCS code(s): _____

   ICD-10-CM code(s): _____

4. Individual treatment of speech and language for patient with articulation disorder due to bilateral conductive hearing loss

CPT code(s): _____

ICD-10-CM code(s): _____, _____

5. Assessment of tinnitus in 55-year-old male with bilateral tinnitus

CPT code(s): _____

ICD-10-CM code(s): _____

Modifiers used in Therapy Services: Two new modifiers were added to the CPT book in 2018, which are designed specifically for therapy services such as those provided by physical, occupational, and speech therapists. Read the following descriptions and uses of these two modifiers, and assign CPT codes (with modifiers) for the cases that follow.

- **Modifier 96, Habilitative Services.** This modifier should be appended to codes for habilitative services that help a patient keep, learn, or improve skills and functions of daily living. For example, an occupational therapy service provided to a pediatric patient with a physical disability that helps the patient learn activities of daily living would be appended with this modifier.

- **Modifier 97, Rehabilitative Services.** This modifier should be appended to codes for rehabilitative services that help a patient keep, recover, or improve skills, functions, and activities of daily living after they have been lost or impaired due to illness, injury, or disability. For example, a physical therapy service provided to an older adult to help him re-learn how to walk after an injury would be classified as a rehabilitative service, and would thus be appended with this modifier.

6. 45 minutes of direct therapeutic activities, including the use of dynamic activities to improve the functional performance of a 4-year-old male patient with congenital deformities of bilateral hands

CPT code(s): _____-_____ (× _____)

ICD-10-CM code(s): _____

7. 30 minutes of therapeutic exercises, focused on range of motion and flexibility of the right knee, status post tear of anterior cruciate ligament of right knee (subsequent encounter)

CPT code(s): _____-_____ (× _____)

ICD-10-CM code(s): _____

CHAPTER

Obstetrics and Gynecology Services

Vocabulary

Instructions: Define each of the following key terms in the space provided.

1. Abortion: _____

_____

_____

2. Antepartum: _____

_____

_____

3. Bartholin's glands: _____

_____

_____

4. Birthing center: _____

_____

_____

5. Cerclage: _____

_____

_____

HCC

6. Certified nurse midwife (CNM): _____

_____

_____

7. Cervix uteri: _____

_____

_____

8. Conization: _____

_____

_____

9. Corpus uteri: _____

_____

_____

10. Diaphragm: _____

_____

_____

11. Endocervical curettage (ECC): _____

_____

_____

12. External os: _____

_____

_____

13. Fallopian tubes: _____

_____

_____

14. Gestation: _____

_____

_____

15. Gestational condition: _____

_____

_____

16. Gravida: _____

_____

_____

17. Gynecologists: _____

_____

_____

18. Incidental pregnancy: _____

_____

_____

19. Internal os: _____

_____

_____

20. Intrauterine device (IUD): _____

_____

_____

21. Introitus: _____

_____

_____

22. Labia majora: _____

_____

_____

23. Labia minora: _____

_____

_____

24. Last menstrual period (LMP): _____

_____

_____

25. Loop electrosurgical excision procedure (LEEP): _____

_____

_____

26. Marsupialization: _____

_____

_____

27. Maternal fetal medicine (MFM) specialist: _____

_____

_____

28. Maternity services: _____

_____

_____

29. Non-obstetric: _____

_____

_____

30. Nuchal cord: _____

_____

_____

31. Nulligravida: _____

_____

32. Nulliparous: _____

_____

_____

33. Obstetric: _____

_____

_____

34. Obstetrics and gynecology services: _____

_____

_____

35. Obstetricians: _____

_____

_____

36. Outcome of delivery code: _____

_____

_____

37. Ovaries: _____

_____

_____

38. Oviducts: _____

_____

_____

39. Parity (or para): _____

_____

_____

40. Perinatal: _____

_____

_____

41. Perinatologist: _____

_____

_____

42. Perineum: _____

_____

_____

43. Peripartum: _____

_____

_____

44. Pessary: _____

_____

_____

45. Postpartum: _____

_____

_____

46. Puerperium: _____

_____

_____

47. Products of conception (POC): _____

_____

_____

48. Reproductive endocrinology and infertility (REI) specialist: _____

_____

_____

49. Reproductive surgery: _____

_____

_____

50. Sequencing priority: _____

_____

_____

51. Trimesters: _____

_____

_____

52. Uterus: _____

_____

_____

53. Vagina: _____

_____

_____

54. Vaginectomy: _____

_____

_____

55. Vulva: _____

_____

_____

Multiple Choice

Instructions: Choose the best answer.

1. Which of the following providers specialize in the health of pregnant patients?
a. Gynecologists
b. Obstetricians
c. Primary care physicians
d. Female wellness practitioners

2. Which of the following providers is a mid-level provider who specializes in the health of pregnant females and in obstetric care?
a. Certified nurse midwife
b. Obstetrician
c. Maternal fetal medicine specialist
d. Gynecologist

3. Which of the following place of service codes would be used for services performed in the labor and delivery (maternity) unit of a hospital facility?
a. 24
b. 11
c. 21
d. 23

4. How many times has a G3P1 patient been pregnant?
   a. 3
   b. 1
   c. 4
   d. Cannot determine from this information

5. Which of the following terms refers to a patient who has never been pregnant?
   a. Multiparous
   b. Multigravida
   c. Gravidanulla
   d. Nulligravida

6. If a patient is at 24 weeks, 3 days' gestation, in which trimester is she?
   a. First
   b. Second
   c. Third

7. Which of the following codes identifies a pregnancy for a patient at 15 weeks' gestation?
   a. O30.892
   b. O30.899
   c. O30.093
   d. O30.099

8. Vulvectomy codes are based on which of the two following principles?
   a. Obstetric and non-obstetric
   b. Depth and size
   c. Extent and depth
   d. Trimester and gravida status

9. Which of the following devices is used as a barrier birth control method?
   a. Cerclage
   b. IUD
   c. Diaphragm
   d. Pessary

10. Which of the following is not included in the global maternity service?
   a. Delivery
   b. Routine antepartum visits
   c. Sick visits
   d. Postpartum visit

Matching

Instructions: Match the female anatomical structure with the code range for procedures on that area.

1. _____ Vulva, perineum and introitus   **A.** 58800 to 58960

2. _____ Vagina   **B.** 58600 to 58770

3. _____ Cervix uteri   **C.** 58100 to 58579

4. _____ Corpus uteri   **D.** 57452 to 57800

5. _____ Oviduct/Ovary   **E.** 57000 to 57426

6. _____ Ovary   **F.** 56405 to 56821

Instructions: Match the type of delivery with its description.

7. _____ Vaginal   **G.** Birth through the natural birth canal after previous surgically-assisted birth

8. _____ Cesarean   **H.** Birth through the natural birth canal

9. _____ Vaginal birth after cesarean   **I.** Surgically-assisted birth in which the infant is delivered through an incision in the lower abdomen

10. _____ Cesarean following attempted VBAC   **J.** Surgically-assisted birth after attempted birth through the natural birth canal after previous surgically-assisted birth

Labeling

Instructions: Complete the following anatomical diagrams with the correct labels to identify the anatomy of the external female genitalia.

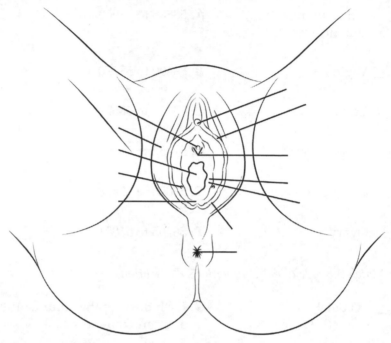

Source: ©AHIMA, figure 17.3, p. 569.

Coding

Instructions: Assign the correct CPT and ICD-10-CM codes for the following.

1. Patient at 30 weeks' gestation presents with polyhydramnios of twin A (fetus 1) in twin gestation.

ICD-10-CM code(s): _____, _____, _____

2. Patient at 38 weeks' gestation and no complications presented to the delivery unit in labor. After 6 hours of natural labor, patient delivered a single, healthy female infant vaginally, without instrumentation, forceps, or episiotomy. OB who performed the delivery is billing for the global maternity service.

CPT code(s): _____

ICD-10-CM code(s): _____, _____, _____

3. G2P2 female presents for delivery at 34 weeks' gestation, and subsequently delivers single liveborn female in breech presentation vaginally. Patient suffered second degree perineal laceration during delivery. (Provide the procedure code for the delivery only.)

CPT code(s): _____

ICD-10-CM code(s): _____, _____, _____,

_____, _____

4. Removal of impacted vaginal foreign body, not requiring general anesthesia. Established patient had a tampon that was she was unable to remove herself. OB/GYN removed the FB without incident from the vagina and performed a detailed history and examination with low complexity MDM.

    CPT code(s): _____

    ICD-10-CM code(s): _____

5. Gonorrhea causing pelvic inflammatory disease (PID) in 23-year-old female patient who commonly engages in high-risk heterosexual behavior. OB/GYN provided a detailed history and examination of this new patient and then spent 30 minutes counseling the patient in ways to reduce chances of obtaining sexually transmitted infections and safe sex techniques. Female also suffers from depression and anxiety and states that sexual deviation is related to these mental health issues.

    CPT code(s): _____

    ICD-10-CM code(s): _____, _____, _____, _____

6. Code for the delivery of a single-live born infant born at 38 weeks' gestation after failed attempted VBAC (infant was born via cesarean section). Previous cesarean was completed with a low transverse incision. (Code for the delivery only.)

    CPT code(s): _____

    ICD-10-CM code(s): _____, _____, _____, _____

7. Elective cesarean delivery completed without complications, resulting in a single, live born female infant at 40 weeks' gestation. OB provided global care for the delivery.

    CPT code(s): _____

    ICD-10-CM code(s): _____, _____, _____

8. Gynecologist performed dilation of urethral stricture under general anesthesia for post-traumatic urethral stricture in a 30-year-old female patient, caused by childbirth.

    CPT code(s): _____

    ICD-10-CM code(s): _____

9. Surgical treatment of incomplete septic abortion due to group A streptococcus.

    CPT code(s): _____

    ICD-10-CM code(s): _____, _____

10. Marsupialization of cyst of Bartholin's gland.

    CPT code(s): _____

    ICD-10-CM code(s): _____

CHAPTER 18

Healthcare Specialist Services, Part I

Vocabulary

Instructions: Define each of the following key terms in the space provided.

1. Alzheimer's disease: _____

_____

_____

2. Anemia: _____

_____

_____

3. Benign prostatic hyperplasia (BPH): _____

_____

_____

4. Brachytherapy: _____

_____

_____

5. Catheterizations: _____

_____

_____

6. Cerebrospinal fluid (CSF) shunt: _____

_____

_____

7. Chemodenervation: _____

_____

_____

8. Chemotherapy: _____

_____

_____

9. Circumcision: _____

_____

_____

10. Consultation: _____

_____

_____

11. Corpora cavernosa: _____

_____

_____

12. Corpora spongiosum: _____

_____

_____

13. Craniectomy: _____

_____

_____

14. Craniotomy: _____

_____

_____

15. Dementia: _____

_____

_____

16. Dialysis: _____

_____

_____

17. Dosimetry: _____

_____

_____

18. Electroencephalogram (EEG): _____

_____

_____

19. Electronic brachytherapy: _____

_____

_____

20. Epididymis: _____

_____

_____

21. Epilepsy: _____

_____

_____

22. Extracorporeal shock wave lithotripsy (ESWL): _____

_____

_____

23. Hematologist: _____

_____

_____

24. Hemodialysis: _____

_____

_____

25. Hydration: _____

_____

_____

26. Hydrocele: _____

_____

_____

27. Infusion: _____

_____

_____

28. Injection: _____

_____

_____

29. Intensity Modulated Radiation Treatment Delivery (IMRT): _____

_____

_____

30. Interstitial brachytherapy: _____

_____

_____

31. Intracavitary brachytherapy: _____

_____

_____

32. Intractable condition: _____

_____

_____

33. Kidney: _____

_____

_____

34. Lower urinary tract symptoms (LUTS): _____

_____

_____

35. Nephrolithiasis: _____

_____

_____

36. Nephrolithotomy: _____

_____

_____

37. Nephrologist: _____

_____

_____

38. Neurologist: _____

_____

_____

39. Neuropsychiatry: _____

_____

_____

40. Neurosurgery: _____

_____

_____

41. Oncologist: _____

_____

_____

42. Orchiopexy: _____

_____

_____

43. Parkinson's disease: _____

_____

_____

44. Penis: _____

_____

_____

45. Peritoneal dialysis: _____

_____

_____

46. Prostate: _____

_____

_____

47. Push: _____

_____

_____

48. Radiation oncologist: _____

_____

_____

49. Scrotum: _____

_____

_____

50. Seminal vesicles: _____

_____

_____

51. Spermatic cord: _____

_____

_____

52. Staghorn calculus: _____

_____

_____

53. Status epilepticus: _____

_____

_____

54. Stereotactic body radiation treatment (SBRT): _____

_____

_____

55. Stereotactic radiosurgery (SRS): _____

_____

_____

56. Testes: _____

_____

_____

57. Transurethral resection of the prostate (TURP): _____

_____

_____

58. Tunica vaginalis: _____

_____

_____

59. Ureters: _____

_____

_____

60. Urethra: _____

_____

_____

61. Urinary bladder: _____

_____

_____

62. Urodynamics: _____

_____

_____

63. Urologist: _____

_____

_____

64. Vas deferens: _____

_____

_____

65. Vasectomy: _____

_____

_____

Fill in the Blank

Instructions: Complete the following statements.

1. List and describe the three Rs of consultations.

a. _____ : _____

_____

b. _____ : _____

_____

c. _____ : _____

_____

2. If a patient's third-party payer, such as Medicare, does not cover consultation services, then the service provided should be reported with the appropriate _____ code (for either the inpatient or outpatient office setting).

3. A _____ is a medical professional who specializes in the diagnosis and treatment of diseases of the blood.

4. A _____ is a medical professional who specializes in the diagnosis and treatment of malignant neoplasms and tumors.

5. A _____ is a medical professional who specializes in the diagnosis and treatment of neurological disorders.

6. A _____ is a medical professional who specializes in the diagnosis and treatment of conditions of the urinary system as well as the male and female genital systems.

7. A _____ is a medical professional who specializes in the diagnosis and treatment of conditions affecting the kidneys.

8. In radiation oncology treatments, _____ is the term used for the calculation of the correct dose amount.

9. The _____ nervous system is composed of the nerves of the brain and the spinal cord, and the _____ nervous system is composed of the nerves throughout the rest of the body.

10. A _____ is a procedure in which a piece of the skull is removed and then replaced, whereas a _____ is a procedure in which a piece of the skull is removed and not replaced.

Matching

Instructions: Match the terms with the appropriate descriptions.

1. _____ Chemotherapy

A. Cancer treatment that involves the insertion of radioactive seeds into body tissues

2. _____ Brachytherapy

B. Involves the removal of malignant tissue

3. _____ Radiation oncology

C. The infusion of chemical substances to treat a malignancy

4. _____ Surgical excision

D. Treatment of malignant neoplasm that involves the use of radioactive treatments

Multiple Choice

Instructions: Choose the best answer.

1. Which of the following identifies the administration of a therapeutic, prophylactic, or diagnostic substance via an IV line, which occurs in 15 minutes or less?
   a. Push
   b. Infusion
   c. Injection
   d. Hydration

2. Which of the following identifies the administration of a therapeutic, prophylactic, or diagnostic substance via an IV line, which occurs in 15 minutes or more?
   a. Push
   b. Infusion
   c. Injection
   d. Hydration

3. Which of the following is the last part of the urinary system, through which urine is eliminated from the body?
   a. Ureter
   b. Urether
   c. Urethra
   d. Ureteral sphincter

4. Which of the following terms identifies a kidney stone?
   a. Renal calculi
   b. Nephrolithotomy
   c. Hepatolithiasis
   d. Cholelithiasis

Coding

Instructions: Report all applicable ICD-10-CM and CPT codes for the following statements.

1. Intermediate proton treatment delivery

   CPT code(s): _____

2. Radiation treatment management involving four treatments

   CPT code(s): _____

3. Complex IMRT delivery

   CPT code(s): _____

4. Complex intracavitary application of brachytherapy source for 65-year-old male patient with prostate cancer that has metastasized to the bladder sphincter

ICD-10-CM code(s): _____, _____

CPT code(s): _____

5. Code for 6 hours and 15 minutes of hydration service via IV line

CPT code(s): _____, _____ × _____

6. Consultation provided to a patient in the inpatient setting, moderate complexity MDM with detailed history and examination

CPT code(s): _____

7. Patient presents for the administration of chemotherapy for metastatic liver cancer

ICD-10-CM code(s): _____, _____

8. Creation of subarachnoid/subdural-auricular shunt for patient with obstructive hydrocephalus

ICD-10-CM code(s): _____

CPT code(s): _____

9. Stereotactic biopsy of lesion of the spinal cord for patient with neoplasm of uncertain behavior of the spinal cord

ICD-10-CM code(s): _____

CPT code(s): _____

10. Extradural laminectomy and excision of neoplasm of the lumbar spinal cord

ICD-10-CM code(s): _____

CPT code(s): _____

11. Digital analysis of EEG for patient with absence epilepsy, intractable, with status epilepticus

ICD-10-CM code(s): _____

CPT code(s): _____

12. Laparoscopic pyeloplasty in 45-year-old male with chronic obstructive pyelonephritis

ICD-10-CM code(s): _____

CPT code(s): _____

13. Transvesical ureterolithotomy for patient with ureteral calculus

ICD-10-CM code(s): _____

CPT code(s): _____

14. Transurethral resection of the prostate due to residual regrowth of prostatic tissue; patient has BPH with the following LUTS: urinary hesitancy, urinary retention, and weak urinary stream

ICD-10-CM code(s): _____, _____,

_____, _____

CPT code(s): _____

15. Linear-based stereotactic radiosurgery (SRS), one session

CPT Code(s): _____

16. Simple intracavitary radiation source application for patient with prostate cancer

ICD-10-CM Code(s): _____

CPT Code(s): _____

17. Infratemporal suture of facial nerve without grafting for a laceration of the nerve of the left cheek

ICD-10-CM Code(s): _____

CPT Code(s): _____

18. Replacement of spinal neurostimulator receiver with direct coupling

CPT code(s): _____

19. Complicated cystorrhaphy for nontraumatic bladder rupture

ICD-10-CM Code(s): _____

CPT Code(s): _____

20. Marsupialization of male urethral diverticulum

ICD-10-CM Code(s): _____

CPT Code(s): _____

CHAPTER 19

Healthcare Specialist Services, Part II

Vocabulary

Instructions: Define each of the following key terms in the space provided.

1. Abdominal aortic aneurysm (AAA): _____

_____

_____

2. Angiography: _____

_____

_____

3. Aneurysm: _____

_____

_____

4. Atherosclerosis: _____

_____

_____

5. Bariatric surgery: _____

_____

_____

6. Cardiac electrophysiology: _____

_____

_____

7. Cardiologist: _____

_____

_____

8. Cardiopulmonary bypass (CPB): _____

_____

_____

9. Cardiothoracic surgery: _____

_____

_____

10. Central venous access devices (CVAD): _____

_____

_____

11. Colonoscopy: _____

_____

_____

12. Colorectal surgery: _____

_____

_____

13. Coronary artery bypass grafts (CABG): _____

_____

_____

14. Coronary artery disease: _____

_____

_____

15. Deep vein thrombosis (DVT): _____

_____

_____

16. Dissecting aneurysm: _____

_____

_____

17. Diverticulitis: _____

_____

_____

18. Diverticulosis: _____

_____

_____

19. Embolus: _____

_____

_____

20. Endovascular procedure: _____

_____

_____

21. Esophagogastroduodenoscopy (EGD): _____

_____

_____

22. Gastric bypass: _____

_____

_____

23. Gastroenterologist: _____

_____

_____

24. Gastro-esophageal reflux disease (GERD): _____

_____

_____

25. Implantable cardiac defibrillator (ICD): _____

_____

_____

26. Non-ruptured aneurysms: _____

_____

_____

27. Pacemaker: _____

_____

_____

28. Patient-activated cardiac event recorder: _____

_____

_____

29. Percutaneous transluminal coronary angioplasty (PTCA): _____

_____

_____

30. Pericardium: _____

_____

_____

31. Proctosigmoidoscopy: _____

_____

_____

32. Pulmonary embolism: _____

_____

_____

33. Ruptured aneurysm: _____

_____

_____

34. Sigmoidoscopy: _____

_____

_____

35. Thrombosis: _____

_____

_____

36. Transluminal procedure: _____

_____

_____

37. Varicose vein: _____

_____

_____

Matching

Instructions: Match the type of pacemaker and implantable cardioverter-defibrillator with its description.

1. _____ Single chamber

A. Leads are placed into the right atrium, left ventricle, and right ventricle

2. _____ Dual chamber

B. Leads are placed into the right atrium and the right ventricle

3. _____ Bi-ventricular pacing

C. Includes a pulse generator and one electrode, placed into the atrium or the ventricle

Instructions: Match the word or term with its description.

4. _____ Patient-activated cardiac event recorder

D. Procedure in which a catheter is inserted into the body, means "inside the vessel"

5. _____ Coronary artery bypass graft

E. X-ray examination of the blood vessels after the administration of a contrast material

6. _____ Endovascular procedure

F. Implanted device that records the electrical activity of the heart when activated by the patient

7. _____ Angioplasty

G. Procedure in which a small piece of vessel is used to bypass a coronary artery

8. _____ Angiography

H. Procedure in which a catheter is inserted into the body, and a balloon is inserted inside the vessel

Multiple Choice

Instructions: Choose the best answer.

1. Which of the following healthcare specialists would perform a heart and lung transplant?
   a. Cardiologist
   b. Gastroenterologist
   c. Cardiothoracic surgeon
   d. Pulmonologist

2. Which of the following healthcare specialists would perform a routine screening colonoscopy, including biopsy of colonic polyps?
   a. Gastroenterologist
   b. Bariatric surgeon
   c. Cardiologist
   d. Urologist

3. A Roux-en-Y procedure is which of the following types of procedures?
   a. Esophagoscopy
   b. Colonoscopy
   c. Intestinal resection
   d. Gastric bypass

4. A screening colonoscopy found a number of small polyps in a patient's transverse colon and a biopsy of the polyps was performed. How should this service be reported?
   a. 45378
   b. 45380
   c. 45378, 45380
   d. 45385

5. Which of the following codes identifies diverticulosis that is occurring in only the small intestine?
   a. K57.12
   b. K57.30
   c. K57.50
   d. K57.10

Coding

Instructions: Report the CPT and ICD-10-CM code(s) from the following diagnostic statements. Pay attention to sequencing conventions and instructions in the Tabular List to ensure that multiple codes are sequenced correctly.

1. Cervical esophagotomy with removal of foreign body due to puncture wound of cervical esophagus, initial encounter

   CPT code(s): _____

   ICD-10-CM code(s): _____

2. Diagnostic flexible transoral esophagoscopy for patient with GERD and esophagitis; multiple biopsies of esophageal tissues were obtained during the procedure

   CPT code(s): _____

   ICD-10-CM code(s): _____

3. Laparoscopic removal of adjustable gastric restrictive device in patient with moderate protein-calorie malnutrition

CPT code(s): _____

ICD-10-CM code(s): _____

4. Enterolysis for adhesions with partial obstruction

CPT code(s): _____

ICD-10-CM code(s): _____

5. Proctosigmoidoscopy with decompression of volvulus

CPT code(s): _____

ICD-10-CM code(s): _____

6. Hartmann type (partial) colectomy for patient with diverticulitis of colon with perforation and abscess with bleeding

CPT code(s): _____

ICD-10-CM code(s): _____

7. Pericardiotomy for removal of intracardiac thrombosis

CPT code(s): _____

ICD-10-CM code(s): _____

8. Insertion of dual transvenous electrodes for implantable defibrillator due to documented non-reversible symptomatic bradycardia due to second degree atrioventricular block

CPT code(s): _____

ICD-10-CM code(s): _____, _____

9. Operative ablation of supraventricular arrhythmogenic pathway for Wolff-Parkinson-White syndrome, without cardiopulmonary bypass

CPT code(s): _____

ICD-10-CM code(s): _____

10. Konno procedure replacement of aortic valve for rheumatic aortic stenosis with insufficiency

CPT code(s): _____

ICD-10-CM code(s): _____

11. CABG utilizing one arterial graft

CPT code(s): _____

12. CABG utilizing four venous grafts harvested from the saphenous vein

CPT code(s): _____

13. Combined coronary artery bypass graft utilizing three venous grafts harvested from the saphenous vein and one arterial graft harvested from the radial artery; patient has atherosclerotic heart disease with angina and is currently dependent on cigarettes, and is also morbidly obese due to excess calories with a BMI of 40.1

CPT code(s): _____, _____, _____

ICD-10-CM code(s): _____

14. Abdominal aortography (S&I only) shows dissection of abdominal aorta

CPT code(s): _____

ICD-10-CM code(s): _____

15. PTCA of left anterior descending artery and left anterior descending diagonal branch in patient with atherosclerosis of native coronary artery of transplanted heart

CPT code(s): _____, _____

ICD-10-CM code(s): _____

CHAPTER

Inpatient Hospital Services

Vocabulary

Instructions: Define each of the following key terms in the space provided.

1. Alteration: _____

_____

_____

2. Bypass: _____

_____

_____

3. Change: _____

_____

_____

4. Code table: _____

_____

_____

5. Control: _____

_____

_____

HCC

6. Creation: _____

_____

_____

7. Delivery: _____

_____

_____

8. Destruction: _____

_____

_____

9. Detachment: _____

_____

_____

10. Device: _____

_____

_____

11. Diagnosis-related groups (DRGs): _____

_____

_____

12. Dilation: _____

_____

_____

13. Division: _____

_____

_____

14. Drainage: _____

_____

_____

15. Excision: _____

_____

_____

16. Extirpation: _____

_____

_____

17. Extraction: _____

_____

_____

18. Fragmentation: _____

_____

_____

19. Fusion: _____

_____

_____

20. Insertion: _____

_____

_____

21. Inspection: _____

_____

_____

22. Map: _____

_____

_____

23. Occlusion: _____

_____

_____

24. Prospective payment system (PPS): _____

_____

_____

25. Qualifier: _____

_____

_____

26. Reattachment: _____

_____

_____

27. Release: _____

_____

_____

28. Removal: _____

_____

_____

29. Repair: _____

_____

_____

30. Replacement: _____

_____

_____

31. Reposition: _____

_____

_____

32. Resection: _____

_____

_____

33. Restriction: _____

_____

_____

34. Revision: _____

_____

_____

35. Root operation: _____

_____

_____

36. Supplement: _____

_____

_____

37. Transfer: _____

_____

_____

38. Transplantation: _____

_____

_____

39. UB-04: _____

_____

_____

Matching

Instructions: Match the type of ICD-10-PCS section with its description.

Section	Definition
1. _____ Medical and Surgical	**A.** Invasive and noninvasive procedures performed on patients, and compiles the vast majority of procedures reported with PCS codes
2. _____ Obstetrics	**B.** Procedures that are not classified elsewhere in the ICD-10-PCS code set and that identify procedures that utilize a new device substance or technology
3. _____ Placement	**C.** Procedures aimed at eliminating substance use, abuse, and dependence, and includes detoxification services and individual counseling
4. _____ Administration	**D.** Procedures that are focused on treating the emotional and behavioral health of the patient, and include crisis intervention and educational and vocational counseling
5. _____ Measurement and Monitoring	**E.** Procedures that identify physical, occupational, and speech language pathology services
6. _____ Extracorporeal Assistance and Performance	**F.** Procedures that utilize radiation to treat cancerous disorders (radiation oncology)
7. _____ Extracorporeal Therapies	**G.** Procedures that introduce radioactive material into the patient in order to create an image of the patient's anatomical structures, such as PET
8. _____ Osteopathic	**H.** Procedures that involve creating images of the patient's anatomical structures, including plain radiography (x-ray), fluoroscopy, CT, MRI, and ultrasound
9. _____ Other Procedures	**I.** Procedures that involve a direct thrust to a joint for the purpose of moving it as a therapeutic treatment
10. _____ Chiropractic	**J.** A miscellaneous range of procedures that do not fall into any other section, including acupuncture, in vitro fertilization, and suture removal
11. _____ Imaging	**K.** Procedures that involve the manual treatment of alleviating somatic dysfunction and related disorders

12. _____ Nuclear Medicine	**L.** Procedures that utilize equipment outside of the body for therapeutic purposes that do not assist or perform a physiological function
13. _____ Radiation Therapy	**M.** Procedures that utilize equipment outside of the body to assist or perform a physiological function
14. _____ Physical Rehabilitation and Diagnostic Audiology	**N.** Procedures that determine the level of a physical or physiological function
15. _____ Mental Health	**O.** Procedures that involve putting in or on a substance used as a therapeutic, diagnostic, nutritional, physiological, or prophylactic
16. _____ Substance Abuse	**P.** Procedures that involve placing an external device in or on a body part in order to protect, immobilize, stretch, compress, or for packing purposes
17. _____ New Technology	**Q.** Procedures performed on the products of conception only, including the fetus, amnion, umbilical cord and placenta

Short Answer

Instructions: Using the given code table, answer the questions that follow.

Section	0	**Medical and Surgical**
Body System	D	**Gastrointestinal System**
Operation	T	**Resection:** Cutting out or off, without replacement, all of a body part

Body Part (4ᵗʰ)	Approach (5ᵗʰ)	Device (6ᵗʰ)	Qualifier (7ᵗʰ)
1 Esophagus, Upper **2** Esophagus, Middle **3** Esophagus, Lower **4** Esophagogastric Junction **5** Esophagus **6** Stomach **7** Stomach, Pylorus **8** Small Intestine **9** Duodenum **A** Jejunum **B** Ileum **C** Ileocecal Valve **E** Large Intestine **F** Large Intestine, Right **H** Cecum **J** Appendix **K** Ascending Colon **P** Rectum **Q** Anus	**0** Open **4** Percutaneous Endoscopic **7** Via Natural or Artificial Opening **8** Via Natural or Artificial Opening Endoscopic	**Z** No Device	**Z** No Qualifier
G Large Intestine, Left **L** Transverse Colon **M** Descending Colon **N** Sigmoid Colon	**0** Open **4** Percutaneous Endoscopic **7** Via Natural or Artificial Opening **8** Via Natural or Artificial Opening Endoscopic **F** Via Natural or Artificial Opening With Percutaneous Endoscopic Assistance	**Z** No Device	**Z** No Qualifier
R Anal Sphincter **U** Omentum	**0** Open **4** Percutaneous Endoscopic	**Z** No Device	**Z** No Qualifier

Source: table 20.3, Casto 2018, 618.

Short Answer continued on next page

(Continued)

1. What does the fifth character identify? _____

2. What body part does the character "T" identify? _____

3. How many different approaches are possible options for the anal sphincter, greater omentum, and lesser omentum? _____

4. What character is used to identify the left large intestine? _____

5. What code would be assigned for the resection of the sigmoid colon via an open approach?

_____

Fill in the Blank

Instructions: Complete the following statements regarding ICD-10-PCS codes.

1. The first character identifies the _____, which is the general type of procedure.

2. The second character identifies the _____, which is the general physiological or anatomical region on which the procedure is performed.

3. The third character identifies the _____, which is the type and objective of the procedure.

4. The fourth character identifies the _____, which is the specific organ or anatomical region involved in the procedure.

5. The fifth character identifies the _____ to the procedure, which is the technique used to gain access to the surgical site.

6. The sixth character identifies the _____ that was used in the procedure, which is any material or appliance that remains after the procedure is performed.

7. The seventh character identifies the _____ for the procedure, which identifies any additional attributes of why or how the procedure was performed.

Reference

Casto, A.B. 2018. ICD-10-PCS Code Book. Chicago: AHIMA.

Appendix A: Student Workbook Answer Key

Chapter 1

Answers to the vocabulary section should be checked using the Medical Coding in the Real World *textbook glossary.*

Matching

1. H

3. G

5. B

7. K

9. R

11. M

13. P

15. N

17. S

19. Q

21. W

23. T

25. X

27. BB

29. A

31. CC

True/False

1. True

3. True

5. False. If you work in a small clinic, you are likely to have to perform multiple responsibilities throughout the clinic.

7. True

9. True

Multiple Choice

1. D

3. B

5. C

7. B

9. B

Chapter 2

Answers to the vocabulary section should be checked using the Medical Coding in the Real World *textbook glossary.*

True/False

1. True

3. True

5. False. The UB-04 form is used for inpatient facility billing, and may also be used to bill for services performed in the outpatient facility setting. The CMS-1500 form is used for outpatient professional billing.

7. True

9. False. Capitation is a form of reimbursement that is based on a per-member per-month payment to the healthcare provider.

Multiple Choice

1. A

3. C

5. B

7. C

9. A

11. B

13. C

15. B

Chapter 3

Answers to the vocabulary section should be checked using the Medical Coding in the Real World *textbook glossary.*

True/False

1. False. Healthcare codes are the numeric or alphanumeric translation of all of the services, supplies, treatments, diagnoses, conditions, and other reasons for healthcare treatments.

3. True

5. False. ICD-10-CM and PCS manuals are published on October 1st of each year.

7. False. Code linkage is linking the diagnosis and procedure code together to identify the medical necessity for the services provided.

9. False. Coding guidelines are the rules that specify what codes to use in which situations, how to sequence them, which modifiers to use, and how to combine them with other codes.

Multiple Choice

1. A
3. C
5. A
7. B
9. A

Short Answer

1. Procedure: Colonoscopy with the removal of two polyps

   Diagnosis: Benign colonic polyps

3. Procedure: Vaginal delivery of newborn

   Diagnosis: 38 weeks' gestation of pregnancy in active labor

5. Because claims are billed to health insurance companies, it is important to understand the many regulations and guidelines that must be followed in order for coders to correctly sequence and report healthcare codes. If the claim is not coded correctly according to the requirements of the third-party payer, then the service may not be reimbursed.

Code Linkage:

1. Box 24.E   Line 1: A

                Line 2: B

                Line 3: B

Chapter 4

Answers to the vocabulary section should be checked using the Medical Coding in the Real World *textbook glossary.*

Fill in the Blank

1. etiology
3. combination
5. not otherwise specified
7. Table of Drugs and Chemicals
9. Table of Neoplasms
11. essential
13. Excludes2
15. Acute
17. Injury mechanism
19. Activity
21. Tabular List

Matching

1. G
3. A
5. D
7. B
9. H
11. I
13. F

Coding

1. Moderate persistent asthma, uncomplicated

   ICD-10-CM code: J45.40

3. Sore throat, fever

   ICD-10-CM code: J02.9, R50.9

5. ICD-10-CM codes: K85.90, K86.1

7. ICD-10-CM code: A24.0

9. ICD-10-CM code: Q80.9

11. ICD-10-CM code: J60

13. ICD-10-CM code: C61, D63.0

15. ICD-10-CM code: B85.0

17. ICD-10-CM codes: T51.2X1A, R07.1

19. ICD-10-CM code: T45.526D

21. ICD-10-CM codes: T51.2X1A, R07.1

23. ICD-10-CM code: T45.526D

25. ICD-10-CM code: M25.531

Answers to questions 26 through 29 must be found by looking up the code descriptions in an ICD-10-CM code book to identify the missing detail.

27. Patient is seen for a *displaced oblique* fracture of the right humerus, *initial encounter for closed fracture*. Fracture was manipulated and immobilized.

29. 2-year-old female presents for treatment for *acute suppurative* otitis media, *without spontaneous rupture of ear drum, recurrent, right ear*

Chapter 5

Answers to the vocabulary section should be checked using the Medical Coding in the Real World *textbook glossary.*

Fill in the Blank

1. 99201–99499

3. 90281–99199, 99500–99607

5. Urinary

7. 61000; 64999

9. subsection

11. category

Matching

1. D

3. C

5. G

7. E

9. H

11. M

13. L

15. K

Coding

1. CPT code(s): 65091

3. CPT code(s): 60520

5. CPT code(s): 92230

7. CPT code(s): 0210T

9. CPT code(s): 15786, 15787

11. CPT code(s): 81402

13. CPT code(s): 53250

15. CPT code(s): 55970

17. CPT code(s): 78607

19. HCPCS code(s): G0442

21. HCPCS code(s): J9027

23. HCPCS code(s): J3060 × 2

25. HCPCS code(s): E0205

27. HCPCS code(s): P9032 × 5

Chapter 6

Answers to the vocabulary section should be checked using the Medical Coding in the Real World *textbook glossary.*

Matching

1. B

3. A

5. E

7. F

9. C

True/False

1. True

3. False. The vehicle used in the ambulance transportation service does impact the code selected.

5. False. Medical necessity does play a part in DMEPOS billing, all services must be considered medically necessary in order to receive reimbursement for the service.

7. True

9. True

Coding

1. HCPCS code(s): A0425 × 15

3. HCPCS code(s): A0430, A0435 × 43

5. Transportation Indicator: C3

7. HCPCS code(s): A0427 –RH, A0425 × 12
ICD-10-CM code(s): R06.02, R07.9

9. HCPCS code(s): A4266
ICD-10-CM code(s): Z30.09

11. HCPCS code(s): E2100
ICD-10-CM code(s): E11.9

13. HCPCS code(s): E0601, A7037
ICD-10-CM code(s): G47.33

15. HCPCS code(s): E0141
ICD-10-CM code(s): R26.0

17. HCPCS code(s): J1630 × 2

19. HCPCS code(s): A9543

21. HCPCS code(s): J0588 × 2

23. HCPCS code(s): A9539

25. HCPCS code(s): E0627

Form for Coding 25 on the next page

Form for Coding 25

DEPARTMENT OF HEALTH AND HUMAN SERVICES
CENTERS FOR MEDICARE & MEDICAID SERVICES

Form Approved
OMB No. 0938-0679

CERTIFICATE OF MEDICAL NECESSITY
CMS-849 — SEAT LIFT MECHANISMS

DME 07.03A

SECTION A: Certification Type/Date: INITIAL ___/___/___ REVISED ___/___/___ RECERTIFICATION___/___/___

PATIENT NAME, ADDRESS, TELEPHONE and HICN	SUPPLIER NAME, ADDRESS, TELEPHONE and NSC or NPI #
Sally B. Good, 1234 Pleasant Road *Pleasantville, TX 12345*	*National Medical Equipment & Supplies* *12345 Medical Lane* *Pleasantville, TX 12345*
(_555_)_987_ - _6543_ HICN _____	(_555_) _576_ - _8542_ NSC or NPI # _123456789_

PLACE OF SERVICE _____	Supply Item/Service Procedure Code(s):	PT DOB _02_/_17_/_65_ Sex _F_ (M/F) Ht._61.5_(in) Wt ___
NAME and ADDRESS of FACILITY *if applicable (see reverse)*	_E0627_ _____ _____ _____	PHYSICIAN NAME, ADDRESS, TELEPHONE and UPIN or NPI # (___) ___-____ UPIN or NPI #_____

SECTION B: Information in this Section May Not Be Completed by the Supplier of the Items/Supplies.

EST. LENGTH OF NEED (# OF MONTHS): _____ 1-99 *(99=LIFETIME)*	DIAGNOSIS CODES: _____ _____ _____ _____

ANSWERS	ANSWER QUESTIONS 1-5 FOR SEAT LIFT MECHANISM (Check Y for Yes, N for No, or D for Does Not Apply)
❏ Y ❏ N ❏ D	1. Does the patient have severe arthritis of the hip or knee?
❏ Y ❏ N ❏ D	2. Does the patient have a severe neuromuscular disease?
❏ Y ❏ N ❏ D	3. Is the patient completely incapable of standing up from a regular armchair or any chair in his/her home?
❏ Y ❏ N ❏ D	4. Once standing, does the patient have the ability to ambulate?
❏ Y ❏ N ❏ D	5. Have all appropriate therapeutic modalities to enable the patient to transfer from a chair to a standing position (e.g., medication, physical therapy) been tried and failed? If YES, this is documented in the patient's medical records.

NAME OF PERSON ANSWERING SECTION B QUESTIONS, IF OTHER THAN PHYSICIAN (Please Print):
NAME: _____ TITLE: _____ EMPLOYER:_____

SECTION C: Narrative Description of Equipment and Cost

(1) Narrative description of all items, accessories and options ordered; (2) Supplier's charge; and (3) Medicare Fee Schedule Allowance for each item, accessory, and option. (see instructions on back)

Electric, separate seat lift mechanism for use with patient's own furniture

SECTION D: PHYSICIAN Attestation and Signature/Date

I certify that I am the treating physician identified in Section A of this form. I have received Sections A, B and C of the Certificate of Medical Necessity (including charges for items ordered). Any statement on my letterhead attached hereto, has been reviewed and signed by me. I certify that the medical necessity information in Section B is true, accurate and complete, to the best of my knowledge, and I understand that any falsification, omission, or concealment of material fact in that section may subject me to civil or criminal liability.

PHYSICIAN'S SIGNATURE_____ DATE ____/____/____
Signature and Date Stamps Are Not Acceptable.

Form CMS-849 (11/11)

Continued on next page

Form for Coding 25, continued

INSTRUCTIONS FOR COMPLETING THE CERTIFICATE OF MEDICAL NECESSITY FOR SEAT LIFT MECHANISMS (CMS-849)

SECTION A:	**(May be completed by the supplier)**
CERTIFICATION DATE:	If this is an initial certification for this patient, indicate this by placing date (MM/DD/YY) needed initially in the space TYPE/ marked "INITIAL." If this is a revised certification (to be completed when the physician changes the order, based on the patient's changing clinical needs), indicate the initial date needed in the space marked "INITIAL," and indicate the recertification date in the space marked "REVISED." If this is a recertification, indicate the initial date needed in the space marked "INITIAL," and indicate the recertification date in the space marked "RECERTIFICATION." Whether submitting a REVISED or a RECERTIFIED CMN, be sure to always furnish the INITIAL date as well as the REVISED or RECERTIFIED date.
PATIENT INFORMATION:	Indicate the patient's name, permanent legal address, telephone number and his/her health insurance claim number (HICN) as it appears on his/her Medicare card and on the claim form.
SUPPLIER INFORMATION:	Indicate the name of your company (supplier name), address and telephone number along with the Medicare Supplier Number assigned to you by the National Supplier Clearinghouse (NSC) or applicable National Provider Identifier (NPI). If using the NPI Number, indicate this by using the qualifier XX followed by the 10-digit number. If using a legacy number, e.g. NSC number, use the qualifier 1C followed by the 10-digit number. (For example. 1Cxxxxxxxxx)
PLACE OF SERVICE:	Indicate the place in which the item is being used, i.e., patient's home is 12, skilled nursing facility (SNF) is 31, End Stage Renal Disease (ESRD) facility is 65, etc. Refer to the DMERC supplier manual for a complete list.
FACILITY NAME:	If the place of service is a facility, indicate the name and complete address of the facility.
SUPPLY ITEM/SERVICE PROCEDURE CODE(S):	List all procedure codes for items ordered. Procedure codes that do not require certification should not be listed on the CMN.
PATIENT DOB, HEIGHT, WEIGHT AND SEX:	Indicate patient's date of birth (MM/DD/YY) and sex (male or female); height in inches and weight in pounds, if requested.
PHYSICIAN NAME, ADDRESS:	Indicate the PHYSICIAN'S name and complete mailing address.
PHYSICIAN INFORMATION:	Accurately indicate the treating physician's Unique Physician Identification Number (UPIN) or applicable National Provider Identifier (NPI). If using the NPI Number, indicate this by using the qualifier XX followed by the 10-digit number. If using UPIN number, use the qualifier 1G followed by the 6-digit number. (For example. 1Gxxxxxx)
PHYSICIAN'S TELEPHONE NO:	Indicate the telephone number where the physician can be contacted (preferably where records would be accessible pertaining to this patient) if more information is needed.
SECTION B:	**(May not be completed by the supplier. While this section may be completed by a non-physician clinician, or a Physician employee, it must be reviewed, and the CMN signed (in Section D) by the treating practitioner.)**
EST. LENGTH OF NEED:	Indicate the estimated length of need (the length of time the physician expects the patient to require use of the ordered item) by filling in the appropriate number of months. If the patient will require the item for the duration of his/her life, then enter "99".
DIAGNOSIS CODES:	In the first space, list the diagnosis code that represents the primary reason for ordering this item. List any additional diagnosis codes that would further describe the medical need for the item (up to 4 codes).
QUESTION SECTION:	This section is used to gather clinical information to help Medicare determine the medical necessity for the item(s) being ordered. Answer each question which applies to the items ordered, checking "Y" for yes, "N" for no, or "D" for does not apply.
NAME OF PERSON ANSWERING SECTION B QUESTIONS:	If a clinical professional other than the treating physician (e.g., home health nurse, physical therapist, dietician) or a physician employee answers the questions of Section B, he/she must print his/her name, give his/her professional title and the name of his/her employer where indicated. If the physician is answering the questions, this space may be left blank.
SECTION C:	**(To be completed by the supplier)**
NARRATIVE DESCRIPTION OF EQUIPMENT & COST:	Supplier gives (1) a narrative description of the item(s) ordered, as well as all options, accessories, supplies and drugs; (2) the supplier's charge for each item(s), options, accessories, supplies and drugs; and (3) the Medicare fee schedule allowance for each item(s), options, accessories, supplies and drugs, if applicable.
SECTION D:	**(To be completed by the physician)**
PHYSICIAN ATTESTATION:	The physician's signature certifies (1) the CMN which he/she is reviewing includes Sections A, B, C and D; (2) the answers in Section B are correct; and (3) the self-identifying information in Section A is correct.
PHYSICIAN SIGNATURE AND DATE:	After completion and/or review by the physician of Sections A, B and C, the physician's must sign and date the CMN in Section D, verifying the Attestation appearing in this Section. The physician's signature also certifies the items ordered are medically necessary for this patient.

Chapter 7

Answers to the vocabulary section should be checked using the Medical Coding in the Real World *textbook glossary.*

Multiple Choice

1. A

3. B

5. B

7. A

9. B

11. D

13. C

15. C

Fill in the Blank

1. Problem focused, expanded problem focused, detailed, comprehensive

3. Straightforward, low, moderate, high

Coding

1. ICD-10-CM code(s): F68.12

3. ICD-10-CM code(s): F65.52

5. ICD-10-CM code(s): F07.81, G44.301

7. CPT code(s): 90839, 90840 × 2

9. CPT code(s): 90791, 90785

11. CPT code(s): 99203
    ICD-10-CM code(s): F40.02

13. CPT code(s): 90791
    ICD-10-CM code(s): F11.251

15. CPT code(s): 99284
    ICD-10-CM code(s): F31.12, F41.0

17. CPT code(s): 99406
    ICD-10-CM code(s): F17.210

19. CPT code(s): 90845
    ICD-10-CM code(s): F91.3

Chapter 8

Answers to the vocabulary section should be checked using the Medical Coding in the Real World *textbook glossary.*

Multiple Choice

1. A

3. B

5. D

7. A

9. D

Completion

1. *Location.* Where on the body the signs or symptoms are present
    Example: throat

3. *Severity.* The intensity of the signs or symptoms, often identified on a scale of 1 to 10
    Example: pain level at a 9/10

5. *Timing.* When the signs or symptoms occur
    Example: every evening or all day long

7. *Modifying factors.* Under what circumstances do the signs or symptoms improve or worsen
    Example: when taking a deep breath

9. *Constitutional.* General constitutional signs or symptoms, such as feeling fatigued or weak

11. *Ears, nose, and throat.* Signs or symptoms involving the ears (such as ringing or pain), the nose (such as rhinorrhea or nose bleeds), and the throat and mouth (such as difficulty swallowing or bleeding gums)

13. *Respiratory.* Signs or symptoms involving the respiratory system, such as shortness of breath, cough, or wheezing

15. *Genitourinary.* Signs or symptoms involving the genitourinary system, such as bedwetting, painful urination, or erectile dysfunction

17. *Integumentary.* Signs or symptoms involving the skin (such as itching or rash) and the breasts (such as breast tenderness or lumps)

19. *Psychiatric.* Signs or symptoms involving the psychiatric system, such as depression or mood swings

21. *Hematologic/lymphatic.* Signs or symptoms involving the hematologic and lymphatic systems, such as bruising easily and swollen glands

Coding

1. Level of HPI: Extended (duration, associated signs and symptoms, timing, modifying factors, context)

3. Level of PFSH: Complete (this is an established patient, which requires one element from each type of history—in this case past allergies and family history of menopause)

5. Level of Examination: Expanded problem focused

7. Amount and/or complexity of data: Minimal

9. Level of MDM: Low

11. ICD-10-CM code(s): E10.9 (long term use of insulin is not reported for Type 1 diabetes mellitus)

13. ICD-10-CM code(s): E11.621, E11.65, L97.421, Z79.4 (uncontrolled diabetes mellitus is codes as diabetes mellitus with hyperglycemia)

15. CPT code(s): 99214

ICD-10-CM code(s): J44.1, J45.41

17. CPT code(s): 99396

ICD-10-CM code(s): Z00.00

19. CPT code(s): 81025

ICD-10-CM code(s): N91.2

21. CPT code(s): 99215

ICD-10-CM code(s): J44.0, J44.1, J20.9, Z87.891

Chapter 9

Answers to the vocabulary section should be checked using the Medical Coding in the Real World *textbook glossary.*

Multiple Choice

1. C

3. A

5. D

7. B

9. A

Labeling

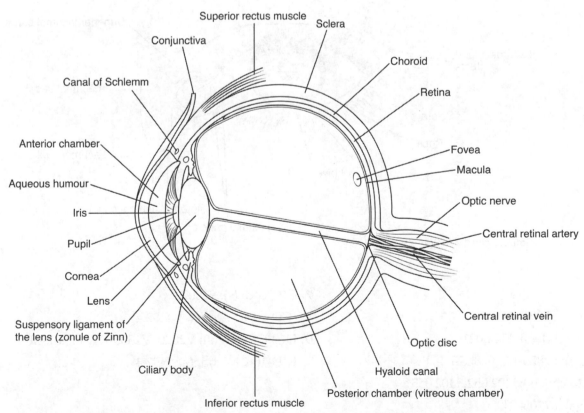

Superior rectus muscle
Sclera
Conjunctiva
Choroid
Canal of Schlemm
Retina
Anterior chamber
Fovea
Aqueous humour
Macula
Iris
Optic nerve
Pupil
Central retinal artery
Cornea
Lens
Central retinal vein
Suspensory ligament of the lens (zonule of Zinn)
Optic disc
Ciliary body
Hyaloid canal
Inferior rectus muscle
Posterior chamber (vitreous chamber)

Source: ©AHIMA, figure 9.2, p. 275.

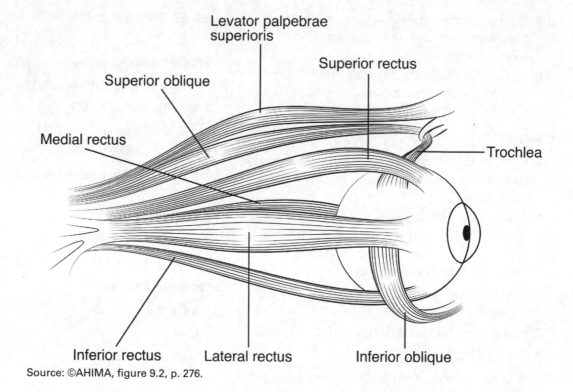

Source: ©AHIMA, figure 9.2, p. 276.

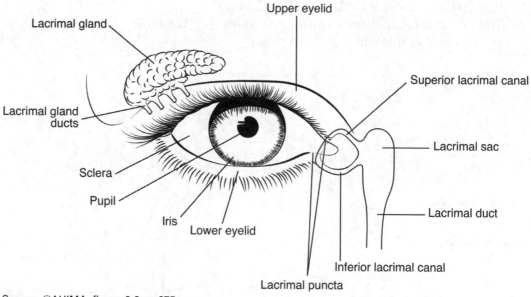

Source: ©AHIMA, figure 9.2, p. 275.

Coding

1. CPT code(s): 65091-RT

ICD-10-CM code(s): H44.021

3. CPT code(s): 67825-E2, 67825-E4

ICD-10-CM code(s): H02.052, H02.055

5. CPT code(s): 67105-RT

ICD-10-CM code(s): H33.011

7. CPT code(s): 92002

ICD-10-CM code(s): H52.4

9. HCPCS code(s): V2020, V2300-RT, V2301-LT

ICD-10-CM code(s): H52.4

Chapter 10

Answers to the vocabulary section should be checked using the Medical Coding in the Real World *textbook glossary.*

Multiple Choice

1. C
3. B
5. D
7. A
9. A

Completion

1. Additional unrelated signs and symptoms?
3. Code for the definitive diagnosis and signs and symptoms

Coding

1. CPT code(s): 99284

   ICD-10-CM code(s): A41.9, R65.20, J96.00
3. ICD-10-CM code(s): I21.4, I48.91
5. ICD-10-CM code(s): F41.0, I25.2
7. CPT code(s): 13100, 12034-59, 12001-59

   ICD-10-CM code(s): S31.131A, S21.111A, S51.812A, S61.412A
9. CPT code(s): 99213-25, 90473, 90660, S9088

   ICD-10-CM code(s): K52.9

CHAPTER 11

Answers to the vocabulary section should be checked using the Medical Coding in the Real World *textbook glossary.*

Word Bank:

Zero Day Global Period	10-Day Global Period	90-Day Global Period
Simple procedure	Minor surgical procedure	Major surgical procedure
Diagnostic endoscopy	Wound repair	Pacemaker insertion

Matching

1. F
3. C
5. K
7. J
9. A
11. L
13. M
15. B

Completion

1. Approach. When coding for an endoscopy, it is necessary to select the code for the correct approach to the procedure. For example, an open approach or through a colostomy.
3. Surgical versus diagnostic procedure. When an endoscopy is done to determine a diagnosis and a surgical procedure is performed during the same endoscopy, then the coder should only report the surgical endoscopy code. For example, a diagnostic bronchoscopy that found polyps and then removed the polyps—then the coder would report only the surgical bronchoscopy, not the diagnostic bronchoscopy.

Coding

1. Modifier: -47
3. Modifier: -66
5. Modifier: -54
7. Modifier: -52
9. Modifier: -23
11. Modifier: -80
13. Modifier: -81
15. Modifier: -56
17. CPT code(s): 60225

    ICD-10-CM code(s): C73, E27.40, E23.0
19. CPT code(s): 42100

    ICD-10-CM code(s): D37.09
21. CPT code(s): 54690-RT

    ICD-10-CM code(s): C62.11
23. CPT code(s): 31299
25. CPT code(s): 31625, 31624-51

    ICD-10-CM code(s): J84.09

Chapter 12

Answers to the vocabulary section should be checked using the Medical Coding in the Real World *textbook glossary.*

Multiple Choice

1. C

3. B

5. D

7. D

Fill in the Blank

1. Base

3. Modifying factors

5. Qualifying circumstances

7. (Base + Time + Modifying Factors) X Conversion Factor = total charge amount

Matching

1. C

3. B

Labeling

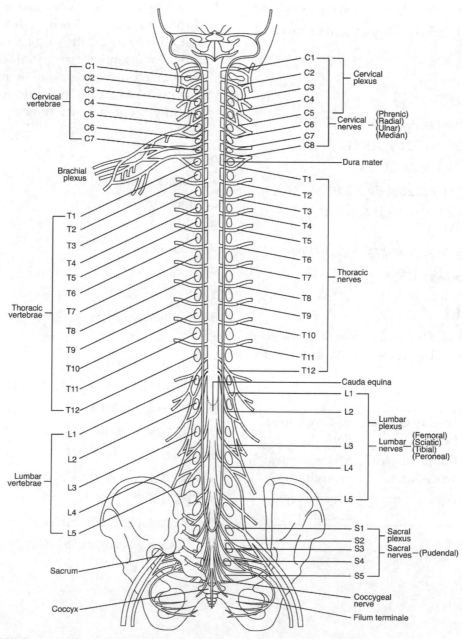

Coding

1. CPT code(s): 00546-P1

3. CPT code(s): 00172-P1

ICD-10-CM code(s): Q35.1

5. CPT code(s): 97813, 97814

ICD-10-CM code(s): M54.41, M54.42

7. CPT code(s): 00921-P1

ICD-10-CM code(s): Z30.2

9. CPT code(s): 64635-50, 64636-50 (× 2)

ICD-10-CM code(s): M54.16

Chapter 13

Answers to the vocabulary section should be checked using the Medical Coding in the Real World *textbook glossary.*

Multiple Choice

1. C

3. D

5. D

7. B

9. A

Matching

1. E

3. H

5. A

7. I

9. F

Coding

1. CPT code(s): 74182

HCPCS code(s): Q9956 x 4

ICD-10-CM code(s): N17.9, R16.0

3. CPT code(s): 76872

ICD-10-CM code(s): N40.0

5. CPT code(s): 78305

ICD-10-CM code(s): M86.161, M86.162

7. CPT code(s): 76770

ICD-10-CM code(s): N20.0

9. CPT code(s): 76819

ICD-10-CM code(s): O99.112

Chapter 14

Answers to the vocabulary section should be checked using the Medical Coding in the Real World *textbook glossary.*

Multiple Choice

1. A

3. B

5. A

Fill in the Blank

1.1 81, Independent lab

1.2 20

1.3 90

1.4 Laboratory CPT code/service

3.1 gross examination

3.2 microscopic examination

3.3 smear

3.4 frozen section

3.5 permanent section

Coding

1. CPT code(s): 36415, 85025

ICD-10-CM code(s): J06.9

3. CPT code(s): 86689

ICD-10-CM code(s): Z21

5. CPT code(s): 88305

ICD-10-CM code(s): N40.0

7. CPT code(s): 86603

ICD-10-CM code(s): J06.9, R19.7

9. CPT code(s): 87110

ICD-10-CM code(s): A56.02, Z72.51

Chapter 15

Answers to the vocabulary section should be checked using the Medical Coding in the Real World *textbook glossary.*

Multiple Choice

1. A

3. D

5. C

7. A

9. C

Matching

1. F

3. C

5. I

7. H

9. A

Coding

1. ICD-10-CM code(s): S79.111A

3. CPT code(s): 29125-RT, 73090-RT

ICD-10-CM code(s): M80.031A

5. CPT code(s): 28810-RT

ICD-10-CM code(s): I96

7. CPT code(s): 20610-RT

ICD-10-CM code(s): M00.061, B95.61

9. CPT code(s): 22015

ICD-10-CM code(s): M46.27

Chapter 16

Answers to the vocabulary section should be checked using the Medical Coding in the Real World *textbook glossary.*

Multiple Choice

1. A

3. B

5. B

Matching

1. C

3. F

5. B

7. G

Coding

1. CPT code(s): 97161

ICD-10-CM code(s): M17.0

3. HCPCS code(s): V5336

ICD-10-CM code(s): R49.1

5. CPT code(s): 92625

ICD-10-CM code(s): H93.13

7. CPT code(s): 97110-97 (× 2)

ICD-10-CM code(s): S83.511D

Chapter 17

Answers to the vocabulary section should be checked using the Medical Coding in the Real World *textbook glossary.*

Multiple Choice

1. B

3. A

5. D

7. A

9. C

Matching

1. F

3. D

5. B

7. H

9. G

Labeling

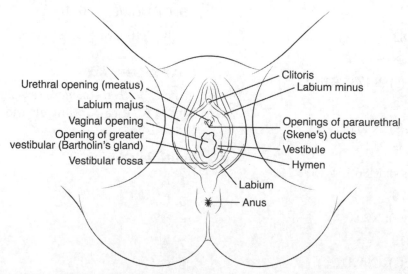

Source: ©AHIMA, figure 17.3, p. 569.

Coding

1. ICD-10-CM code(s): O40.3XX1, O30.003, Z3A.30

3. CPT code(s): 59409

   ICD-10-CM code(s): O60.14X0, O32.1XX0, O70.1, Z37.0, Z3A.34

5. CPT code(s): 99203

   ICD-10-CM code(s): A54.24, Z72.51, F32.9, F41.9

7. CPT code(s): 59510

   ICD-10-CM code(s): N35.021

9. CPT code(s): 59830

   ICD-10-CM code(s): O03.87, B95.0

Chapter 18

Answers to the vocabulary section should be checked using the Medical Coding in the Real World *textbook glossary.*

Fill in the Blank

1. A. Request: Patient's provider requests the consultation

   B. Render: Consultant renders the consultation

   C. Report: Consultant send written report to provider

3. Hematologist

5. Neurologist

7. Nephrologist

9. Central; peripheral

Matching

1. C

3. D

Multiple Choice

1. A

3. C

Coding

1. CPT code(s): 77523

3. CPT code(s): 77386

5. CPT code(s): 96360, 96361 × 5

7. ICD-10-CM code(s): Z51.11, C78.7

9. CPT code(s): 63615

   ICD-10-CM code(s): D43.4

11. CPT code(s): 95957

    ICD-10-CM code(s): G40.A11

13. CPT code(s): 51060

    ICD-10-CM code(s): N20.1

15. CPT code(s): 77372

17. CPT code(s): 64865

    ICD-10-CM code(s): S04.52XA

19. CPT code(s): 51865

    ICD-10-CM code(s): N32.89

Chapter 19

Answers to the vocabulary section should be checked using the Medical Coding in the Real World *textbook glossary.*

Matching

1. C

3. A

5. G

7. H

Multiple Choice

1. C

3. D

5. D

Coding

1. CPT code(s): 43020

   ICD-10-CM code(s): S11.24XA

3. CPT code(s): 43772

   ICD-10-CM code(s): E44.0

5. CPT code(s): 45321

   ICD-10-CM code(s): K56.2

7. CPT code(s): 33020

   ICD-10-CM code(s): I51.3

9. CPT code(s): 33250

   ICD-10-CM code(s): I45.6

11. CPT code(s): 33533

13. CPT code(s): 33533, 33519, 35600

    ICD-10-CM code(s): I25.119, F17.210, E66.01, Z68.41

15. CPT code(s): 92920, 92921

    ICD-10-CM code(s): I25.811

Chapter 20

Answers to the vocabulary section should be checked using the Medical Coding in the Real World *textbook glossary.*

Matching

1. A
3. P
5. N
7. L
9. J
11. H
13. F
15. D
17. B

Short Answer

1. Approach to the procedure
3. 2; open and percutaneous endoscopic
5. 0DTN0ZZ

Fill in the Blank

1. Section
3. Root Operation or Type
5. Approach
7. Qualifier

Appendix B: Additional Resources

The following is a list of suggested resource materials for medical coding students to be used in addition to the textbook and student workbook.

Code books that are referenced in the textbook:

- ICD-10-CM (current year)
- ICD-10-PCS (current year)
- ICD-9 (as a reference for the legacy system)
- CPT (current year)
- HCPCS (current year)

A medical dictionary for health professionals, such as Mosby. 2017. *Mosby's Medical Dictionary,* Tenth Edition. St. Louis, MO: Elsevier.

Coding certification study guides:

- American Health Information Management Association. 2018. *CCS Exam Preparation*, Eighth Edition. Chicago: AHIMA.
- American Health Information Management Association. 2017. *Certified Coding Associate (CCA) Exam Preparation, Sixth Edition.* Chicago: AHIMA.
- National Healthcareer Association. *Certified Billing & Coding Specialist (CBCS) Printed Study Guide.* Leawood, KS: NHA.
- American Academy of Professional Coders. 2018. *Official CPC Certification Study Guide.* Salt Lake City: AAPC.

American Medical Association. 2017. *Advanced Anatomy and Physiology for ICD-10-CM/PCS 2018.* Chicago: AMA.

American Psychiatric Association. 2013. *Diagnostic and Statistical Manual of Mental Disorders (DSM-5®), Fifth Edition.* Washington, DC: APA.

American Society of Anesthesiologists. 2018. *Crosswalk 2018.* Schaumburg, IL: ASA.

Appendix C: Blank Forms

CMS-1500

HEALTH INSURANCE CLAIM FORM

APPROVED BY NATIONAL UNIFORM CLAIM COMMITTEE (NUCC) 02/12

| | PICA | | | | | | PICA | |

1. MEDICARE (Medicare#) **MEDICAID** (Medicaid#) **TRICARE** (ID#/DoD#) **CHAMPVA** (Member ID#) **GROUP HEALTH PLAN** (ID#) **FECA BLK LUNG** (ID#) **OTHER** (ID#) | **1a. INSURED'S I.D. NUMBER** (For Program in Item 1)

2. PATIENT'S NAME (Last Name, First Name, Middle Initial) | **3. PATIENT'S BIRTH DATE** MM DD YY **SEX** M F | **4. INSURED'S NAME (Last Name, First Name, Middle Initial)**

5. PATIENT'S ADDRESS (No., Street) | **6. PATIENT RELATIONSHIP TO INSURED** Self Spouse Child Other | **7. INSURED'S ADDRESS (No., Street)**

CITY STATE | **8. RESERVED FOR NUCC USE** | CITY STATE

ZIP CODE TELEPHONE (Include Area Code) ( ) | | ZIP CODE TELEPHONE (Include Area Code) ( )

9. OTHER INSURED'S NAME (Last Name, First Name, Middle Initial) | **10. IS PATIENT'S CONDITION RELATED TO:** | **11. INSURED'S POLICY GROUP OR FECA NUMBER**

a. OTHER INSURED'S POLICY OR GROUP NUMBER | **a. EMPLOYMENT? (Current or Previous)** YES NO | **a. INSURED'S DATE OF BIRTH** MM DD YY **SEX** M F

b. RESERVED FOR NUCC USE | **b. AUTO ACCIDENT?** YES NO **PLACE (State)** | **b. OTHER CLAIM ID (Designated by NUCC)**

c. RESERVED FOR NUCC USE | **c. OTHER ACCIDENT?** YES NO | **c. INSURANCE PLAN NAME OR PROGRAM NAME**

d. INSURANCE PLAN NAME OR PROGRAM NAME | **10d. CLAIM CODES (Designated by NUCC)** | **d. IS THERE ANOTHER HEALTH BENEFIT PLAN?** YES NO *If yes,* complete items 9, 9a, and 9d.

READ BACK OF FORM BEFORE COMPLETING & SIGNING THIS FORM.
12. PATIENT'S OR AUTHORIZED PERSON'S SIGNATURE I authorize the release of any medical or other information necessary to process this claim. I also request payment of government benefits either to myself or to the party who accepts assignment below.

SIGNED _____ DATE _____ | **13. INSURED'S OR AUTHORIZED PERSON'S SIGNATURE** I authorize payment of medical benefits to the undersigned physician or supplier for services described below.

SIGNED _____

14. DATE OF CURRENT ILLNESS, INJURY, or PREGNANCY (LMP) MM DD YY QUAL. | **15. OTHER DATE** QUAL. MM DD YY | **16. DATES PATIENT UNABLE TO WORK IN CURRENT OCCUPATION** FROM MM DD YY TO MM DD YY

17. NAME OF REFERRING PROVIDER OR OTHER SOURCE | 17a. 17b. NPI | **18. HOSPITALIZATION DATES RELATED TO CURRENT SERVICES** FROM MM DD YY TO MM DD YY

19. ADDITIONAL CLAIM INFORMATION (Designated by NUCC) | **20. OUTSIDE LAB?** YES NO **$ CHARGES**

21. DIAGNOSIS OR NATURE OF ILLNESS OR INJURY Relate A-L to service line below (24E) ICD Ind.
A. B. C. D.
E. F. G. H.
I. J. K. L. | **22. RESUBMISSION CODE** ORIGINAL REF. NO. **23. PRIOR AUTHORIZATION NUMBER**

24. A. DATE(S) OF SERVICE From MM DD YY To MM DD YY	B. PLACE OF SERVICE	C. EMG	D. PROCEDURES, SERVICES, OR SUPPLIES (Explain Unusual Circumstances) CPT/HCPCS MODIFIER	E. DIAGNOSIS POINTER	F. $ CHARGES	G. DAYS OR UNITS	H. EPSDT Family Plan	I. ID. QUAL.	J. RENDERING PROVIDER ID. #
1									NPI
2									NPI
3									NPI
4									NPI
5									NPI
6									NPI

25. FEDERAL TAX I.D. NUMBER SSN EIN | **26. PATIENT'S ACCOUNT NO.** | **27. ACCEPT ASSIGNMENT?** (For govt. claims, see back) YES NO | **28. TOTAL CHARGE** $ | **29. AMOUNT PAID** $ | **30. Rsvd for NUCC Use**

31. SIGNATURE OF PHYSICIAN OR SUPPLIER INCLUDING DEGREES OR CREDENTIALS (I certify that the statements on the reverse apply to this bill and are made a part thereof.)
SIGNED _____ DATE _____ | **32. SERVICE FACILITY LOCATION INFORMATION** a. NPI b. | **33. BILLING PROVIDER INFO & PH #** ( ) a. NPI b.

NUCC Instruction Manual available at: www.nucc.org — *PLEASE PRINT OR TYPE* — APPROVED OMB-0938-1197 FORM 1500 (02-12)

UB-04 / CMS-1450

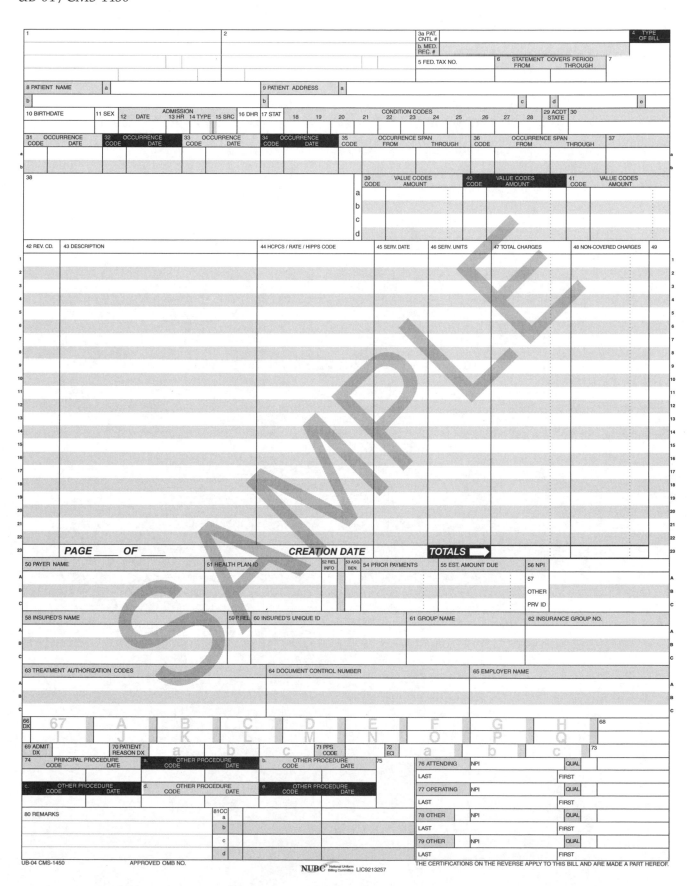

UB-04 CMS-1450   APPROVED OMB NO.   **NUBC**® National Uniform Billing Committee LIC9213257   THE CERTIFICATIONS ON THE REVERSE APPLY TO THIS BILL AND ARE MADE A PART HEREOF.

Trust AHIMA for Your Coding Education and Training

AHIMA is widely recognized and highly regarded as a leader in coding education and training. AHIMA has been at the forefront of providing coding expertise for over 85 years and served as one of four cooperating parties responsible for the ICD-10 Coding Guidelines.

AHIMA HAS A VARIETY OF CODING PRODUCTS AND RESOURCES TO ASSIST YOU AND YOUR TEAM:

- Professional Books and Textbooks
- Meetings
  - In-Person
  - Virtual
- Online Courses
- Toolkits and Practice Briefs
- Webinars

For a complete list of all AHIMA coding products and resources, visit ahimastore.org.

American Health Information Management Association®

1330.16

PREPARE FOR YOUR FUTURE WITH AHIMA MEMBERSHIP

Are you ready for a job in health information (HI)? Seeking to take steps toward a successful career path? Get started with an AHIMA student membership! Join AHIMA today and gain multiple professional benefits. Our resources will prepare you to find one of the thousands of projected new HIM jobs.

EXCEL IN SCHOOL AND PLAN FOR YOUR FUTURE WITH AHIMA MEMBER BENEFITS!

- Follow industry news in the digital edition of the *Journal of AHIMA*, *CareerMinded*, and other e-newsletters

- Explore the job market through Career Assist: Job Bank

- Find someone to listen and look up to through AHIMA's mentor program

- Discounts on books, events, webinars, credentials, and more

- Get ready to enter the job market with AHIMA's career prep resources, including free webinars, a toolkit, and the HIM Career Map

- Build your resume with volunteer opportunities

- Network locally with component state association (CSA) membership

- AHIMA's new Body of Knowledge (BoK), an online HIM library, makes study and research a breeze

- Interact with HIM professionals and fellow students on AHIMA's Engage Online Communities

- Free admission to the AHIMA Convention Student Academy

- AHIMA Foundation Merit Scholarships available

JOIN TODAY AT AHIMA.ORG/JOIN.

278.16